D1309188

**VOLUME
22**

Originally published in the United Kingdom in weekly parts **COMBAT & SURVIVAL** is a study of the armed forces at work. It shows the skills taught to soldiers and the way in which military units operate. It examines the weapons and equipment used by different armies; and, by looking at recruit training and exercises, **COMBAT & SURVIVAL** demonstrates how the armed forces develop individual responsibility, leadership and initiative.

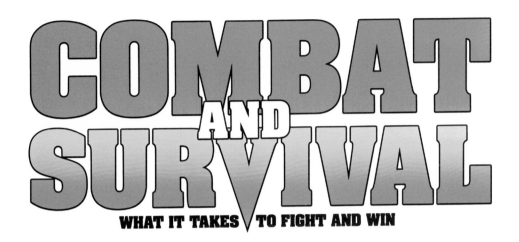

COMBAT AND SURVIVAL

WHAT IT TAKES TO FIGHT AND WIN

VOLUME
22

H. S. STUTTMAN, INC. *publishers*   Westport, Connecticut 06889

Contents
Volume 22

Published by H. S. STUTTMAN INC.
Westport, Connecticut 06889
© Aerospace Publishing 1991
ISBN 0-87475-560-3

All individual combat and personal survival activities involve risk or injury, to oneself and others, and great care must be taken in carrying out any such activities. Expert guidance should be sought and equipment checked for reliability before any activities described in this work are carried out. The publishers cannot assume responsibility for damage to property or injury, death or loss to persons which may result from carrying out the activities described in this work. In carrying out any activities described in this work, persons do so entirely at their own risk.
PRINTED IN THE UNITED STATES OF AMERICA

1P(1632)30

ANTI-TERRORIST OPERATIONS

FIGHTING IN THE BUSH

1. You must tailor your weapons and equipment to the terrain. Ammunition and water supplies are particularly critical.

2. In Rhodesia you could usually count on air cover, but now that Cuban-flown MiG-23s are operating from Angola air superiority can no longer be taken for granted.

3. Anti-terrorist operations require excellent leadership at section and platoon level: it is often a junior commanders' war.

4. Study the enemy. The African guerrilla is trained very differently from European troops, and will frequently react in an unexpected way.

"Rhodesia's Security Forces are potentially among the best in the world. This potential will only be realised by hard training and sound knowledge ..." So reads part of the Preface to the 1975 edition of the Rhodesian Security Force's COIN Manual (II).

The outcome of the Rhodesian war was ultimately decided by politicians at Lancaster House, in London. It was a dreadfully bitter blow for the Security Forces, who continued to triumph in the bush right until the very end. The lessons they learned, improved on and refined during 14 years of conflict cannot be ignored. They are as true of Africa today as they ever were!

The terrain in southern Africa varies greatly, ranging from thick vegetation through semi-desert to

A Kraal that had been used as a guerrilla base during the Rhodesian war is burned. Separating the population from the guerrillas proved an impossible task during the Rhodesian war and the security forces gradually lost control of the countryside, especially during the hours of darkness.

mountainous areas. Troop deployment is also affected by the climate, with its distinct dry and rainy seasons. Usually, things tend to quieten down during the wet weather, with neither side wishing to operate in cold, dense fog and torrential rain. Sometimes, terrorists will take advantage of adverse conditions to move quietly in or out of an area.

Climate effect

Terrain and climate may hamper vehicles and reduce radio transmission and reception ranges. The climate will also affect unfit troops and those not immunised against tropical

Most Rhodesian soldiers wore a mixture of civilian and customised kit, but this trooper wears full regulation equipment. He is carrying a radio with the handset tied to the webbing shoulder strap and the aerial tucked down to keep it inconspicuous.

In African wars past and present, weapons and equipment now obsolete in Europe continue to give good service. The Ferret armoured car remains an African and Asian favourite because it is simple to maintain and spare parts are plentiful.

diseases. In addition, wild mammals, insects and reptiles are abundant and call for extra precautionary measures.

Enemy forces

In southern and central Africa, the enemy is very different from any likely to be encountered in other theatres of war. This statement should not be misconstrued as racist. It is a simple fact. A young newcomer to Rhodesia received the following advice on the African terrorist: "Don't make the mistake of thinking they're like us. When you want to figure out how a terr might react, think how you would behave in his situation. The

chances are, he will do the opposite . . ."

Study the enemy. Find out what his weaknesses are. Learn from his strengths. As in any war, do not underestimate him! Unfortunately, too many soldiers in Africa have shown little respect for their adversary – and paid the ultimate price.

The African terrorist can be a man or woman. Combatants are usually fairly young, ranging in age from late teens to late twenties. In general, few are especially well trained. However, most know how to aim and fire a rifle or machine gun and how to throw a grenade. What the terrorist lacks in military skills, he makes up for in a natural understanding of the bush. He is usually extremely fit, and able to move on foot at an alarming pace. Perhaps his main advantage is his ability to blend with the local inhabitants – in effect, to disappear.

The rural terrorist is usually fairly well-equipped with the SKS and ubiquitous AK rifles. Machine guns frequently consist of RPDs and RPKs. Many groups also carry RPG 2 and RPG 7 rocket launchers. Grenades are abundant, especially the Chinese stick and Soviet F1 type.

Friendly regulars

As part of a regular unit, you are considerably better off than your adversary.

In Rhodesia, a typical "Fire Force" stick consisted of four men. The stick

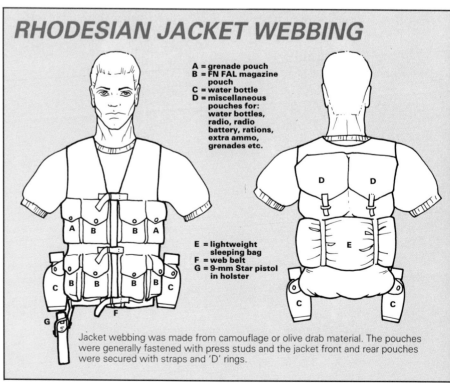

RHODESIAN JACKET WEBBING

A = grenade pouch
B = FN FAL magazine pouch
C = water bottle
D = miscellaneous pouches for: water bottles, radio, radio battery, rations, extra ammo, grenades etc.

E = lightweight sleeping bag
F = web belt
G = 9-mm Star pistol in holster

Jacket webbing was made from camouflage or olive drab material. The pouches were generally fastened with press studs and the jacket front and rear pouches were secured with straps and 'D' rings.

Above: The assault course of the Rhodesian Light Infantry stretched even the fittest troops. African guerrilla troops, inured to physical hardship, are exceptionally fit and can move with bewildering rapidity through the bush.

The assault course is tackled with belt order and rifle – although one soldier humps an FN MAG. These GPMGs provided the bulk of the RLI's firepower, equipping one man in every four-man stick.

Hand over hand in the issue kit which proved inadequate for the 'Fire Force' encounters. The trousers seen here were often split below the knee so that you could pull them quickly over your boots in the event of a call-out.

leader, usually an NCO, was equipped with a map and radio and took his orders from an officer circling in a helicopter overhead. The stick leader and two of his troopers were armed with 7.62-mm FN rifles. The two riflemen took it in turns to carry a well-stocked medical pack. (Like the radio, it was an item often lacking among terrorist groups.)

A fourth trooper was armed with a 7.62-mm FN MAG (machine gun). He was invariably the biggest man in the stick, as he had to be able to carry the heavy weapon for hours at a time – and still be able to provide the group's

Rear view of the Rhodesian jacket webbing, with lightweight sleeping bag fixed underneath the top pouches. Since the Rhodesian war, assault vest-type chest webbing has become popular with many Special Forces units and many versions are now available.

GUN WEBBING AND 'GOOK' CHEST WEBBING

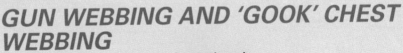

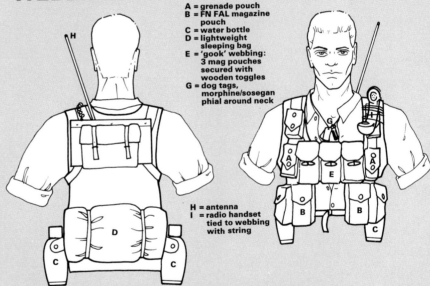

A = grenade pouch
B = FN FAL magazine pouch
C = water bottle
D = lightweight sleeping bag
E = 'gook' webbing: 3 mag pouches secured with wooden toggles
G = dog tags, morphine/sosegan phial around neck

H = antenna
I = radio handset tied to webbing with string

Both types of webbing shown here and to the left were manufactured in a shop called 'Feredays' in Salisbury. The A63 radio could be carried in its own back pack, in the back pouch of the jacket webbing or in the belt order side pouch. The handset was usually secured to the webbing shoulder strap. There was an infinite variety of webbing used during the Rhodesian war, it all depended on what you liked and what was available. Captured Chinese issue water bottles could be slung or worn on the belt. Yokes were usually attached too, along with a knife and a holster for whatever type of pistol the soldier carried. Many Rhodesian troops preferred captured SKS or AK slings to the issue variety.

BELT ORDER

Belt order could consist of virtually any combination of assorted pouches. Here we have a pair of British G7098 side pouches for magazines, a couple of Rhodesian water bottles and carriers, a Chinese or East German ammo/grenade pouch, and two Rhodesian grenade pouches.

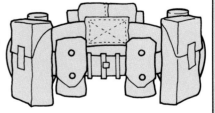

Rhodesian soldiers dubbed their enemies 'gooks', 'floppies', or 'terrs' depending on their previous military experience. Some French troops with memories of Algeria even called them 'fellahs'. This guerrilla is unusual, apparently wearing WW II US webbing.

Another captured guerrilla photograph probably shows a member of ZANLA wearing Portuguese army camouflage trousers and carrying a Soviet Degtyarev 7.62-mm machine-gun. Although introduced in 1928, the DP is a solid LMG, and tolerates primitive conditions very well.

Posing rather glumly, this guerrilla's webbing looks home-made and its tattered state indicates that he has spent a fair time in the bush. Radio/cassette players were very popular with the guerrillas and were often captured in enemy camps.

main fire power. He was often required to fire the MAG from the hip, and even from the shoulder! Extra rounds for the gun were distributed among the stick. Everyone carried grenades. Most soldiers preferred a generous mix of HE and WP grenades in addition to smoke.

Handguns were sometimes carried. The 9-mm Star was the standard issue pistol, but was not highly thought of. Soldiers preferred to carry privately owned handguns – anything from a

These are probably ZANLA guerrillas wearing a typical mixture of equipment, but all with Kalashnikovs. Sometimes short of ammunition by the late 1970s, the Rhodesian troops were always keen to kill guerrillas armed with a G3 or FAL so that they could use their rounds.

.38 S&W snub-nose, to 9-mm Brownings and .44 Magnums! Knives were another personal choice, with the weapon kept in a scabbard on a belt, or secured to a shoulder strap.

Dress easy

In the bush there were no dress regulations. You wore what was most comfortable and functional – an arrangement other armies could well emulate. A combination of shorts, tee-shirts and tennis shoes was not unusual, although many chose to wear camouflage overalls and slightly more robust footwear. Webbing was another personal preference. Hardly anybody cared for issue equipment, and instead wore custom-made jacket, gun or chest webbing. The

latter was based on the excellent webbing worn by the enemy. After some modification, captured enemy webbing was also an ideal choice.

In Africa, the big advantage you should have over the enemy is that of air cover. Although sometimes equipped with modern jet aircraft, most Third World countries still lack sufficient trained personnel to keep them flying. Soviet, East German and Cuban "advisors" are on hand, but it is rare to encounter them in a battle area.

Below: South African horsemen on exercise, armed with R4 rifles. In Rhodesia, Grey's Scouts and other mounted infantry units demonstrated the continuing value of the horse in African warfare.

Left and above: After the defeat of the Ian Smith government, many Rhodesian veterans moved to South Africa where their professional expertise was also in demand. Here they undergo selection for the Pathfinder company in the South African Army's 44 Para Brigade.

Command and control

Because of their peculiar nature, anti-terrorist operations (ATOPS) demand much more of the junior leader than does conventional warfare. To seek out and destroy an elusive enemy, ATOPS are based on a pattern of small units tasked with locating and/or eliminating the enemy. Frequently, small groups are required to operate alone, far from base, for long periods. Consequently, junior leaders often have to make rapid, on the spot decisions.

It frequently happens that a junior commander is the sole representative of military authority in a large area. He must then be able to communicate with civil authorities and the local population. Such a role demands a high degree of tact, understanding, diplomacy and sound judgement.

Who does what best

Armoured vehicles in ATOPS are usually restricted by terrain and other factors. They may be used on road escort and patrol duties or as road blocks. Armoured cars can also be used as a show of force, or to protect certain sensitive points. Occasionally, they may be used in support of infantry.

Rhodesia's Grey's Scouts proved that there is plenty of scope for mounted troops in bush warfare. Compared to the infantryman, a horse can carry more weight and move at a faster pace for far longer. However, there are places where even a horse cannot effectively operate.

Artillery, Engineers and supporting units all have a role to play, but it is the infantryman who must ultimately bear the brunt of the fighting.

Against a guerrilla opponent with few anti-aircraft weapons. World War II style para-drops can still work. Rhodesian paratroopers who joined the SADF after 1979 were impressed to find themselves jumping from some of the same aircraft they had used during the war. They recognised the cannon holes.

Combat Report
Rhodesia:
Guerrilla Contact in the Bush War Part 1

A technician/gunner with the Rhodesian Air Force describes a large-scale guerrilla contact while on operations with 1 Para's Fire Force.

I woke at first light, my brain going into immediate panic-mode, thinking I'd slept in. But the five others in the tent were still asleep and I remembered that we had nothing planned for this morning.

We operated the Alouette III in two roles. The G-car carried pilot, gunner and a stick of four troops and had a side-mounted twin-Browning gunfit. The other role was the K-car, armed with a side-mounted 20-mm Mauser cannon and carrying pilot, gunner and observer, usually a senior officer of whichever army unit we were operating with. The K-car would orbit at a few hundred feet, directing operations and laying down covering fire.

The Fire Force operation also had a Dakota for para-dropping, and air strikes using Hunters could be called upon if needed. The idea was to have a mobile unit that could be positioned at short notice at one of the many forward airfields around the country.

Waiting for a call-out

We had been directed to Plumtree on the Rhodesia/Botswana border after receiving intelligence of guerrilla activity in the area. We had been there for five days but had not had any contact with the terrs, which is the way it goes sometimes.

I got up, pulled on a jumper over my bush shirt and wandered out into the cold African morning. I made my way across to my machine and busied myself with the endless minor tasks that kept it in good working order, then cleaned the cannon (which I had given a thorough cleaning the previous evening, but once more wouldn't hurt) and did a quick check of the equipment. Then I wandered back to rouse the rest of the sleeping crews.

They were up by the time I returned – probably the smell of breakfast from the mess tent had woken them. We strolled over for some food. By the time we had finished it was full daylight and we lounged around, drinking tea and waiting for a call-out.

Nothing happened, however, and it was decided that morning to pack up and go home to Salisbury. We had started packing our kit when the adjutant's loud-hailer rudely interrupted us. "Call-out, call-out!" The three pilots hurried over to the ops tent for a briefing while I and the other two techs dashed to the choppers and made ready to get airborne. The paras were struggling into their kit and making their way across to the Dak, which already had both engines burning and turning.

The pilots arrived and a short while later we were airborne, heading towards the target at treetop height. Apparently one of the patrols sent out by Fire Force had come across fresh spoor coming in from Botswana, a group of between 30 and 40, headed towards one of the large tobacco estates found in that part of the world. K-car commander, the para colonel, was busy in his observer's seat looking at a map and plotting the terrs' possible route and target.

"K-car lifting now!"

"Those monkeys are headed right towards one of our OPs on top of this gomo here," he said, showing the map to the pilot.

"If the spoor is not much more than one hour old, we should make contact about here," said the pilot, pointing to the map. "Estimate 12

minutes."

The colonel passed this info back to base and instructed 'Landtail', a convoy of three trucks carrying fuel for the choppers as well as ammo and first aid, to head towards the contact area and hold its position about one kilometre away, making sure that there would be a suitable LZ for the choppers. The Dak was to stand by, ready for take-off.

A few minutes later the pilot reported "K-car lifting now." This was the moment that K-car left the formation and lifted into an orbit around the probable target area, while the pilot, K-car commander and myself strained our eyes for signs of the terrs on the ground below. It was also the time when we could take a lot of flak, as we would be presenting the first target of the contact.

We circled the area for a couple of minutes without seeing anything. We weren't helped by the terrain, which consisted of several granite kopjes covered with large boulders and scree, with a thick covering of bush in a few places. The ground between the kopjes was fairly broken, criss-crossed with shallow ravines and gullies, with isolated pockets of bush thrown in: not the best of places to find people who didn't want to be found. Unless they moved, we weren't going to see them from the air. We climbed higher to increase our field of vision.

"They should be here by now," muttered the colonel. "Stick four, nine. Stick four, nine." Stick four was the OP.

Which way had they gone?

"Nine, stick four. Reading you fives."

"Stick four, any visual on terrs?"

"Negative. They are not in our field of vision." This meant that they had either stopped or changed direction. If they had stopped, the patrol that was following the spoor would have contacted them by now. If they had changed direction, which way had they gone? The orbiting K-car would have alerted them to our presence and they would be waiting for us.

"Nine, this is three two." Three two was the patrol on spoor.

"Three two, nine."

"Nine, spoor is veering away. Heading east-south-east, repeat east-south-east."

"Roger, three two, keep on spoor."

"Three two."

The colonel consulted his map. Armed with this new info, we moved our search area slightly to the south, to an area dominated by three large kopjes. We took up orbit around the kopje nearest the trackers, searching the ground for

movement. The colonel called in the G-cars.

"G-one, nine."

"Nine. G-one receiving you fives."

"G-one, put your stick down on the western end of the kopje we're circling, as close as you can to that long, flat boulder. They can work their way up to the top and along the ridge."

"Confirm western end?"

"Western end. Close to the flat boulder, at the bottom of the small gully."

"G-one."

The G-car began his descent, picking out a likely LZ as close as possible to the desired spot, then going in quickly, his gunner talking him down. The four-man stick departed the chopper before the wheels hit the deck. G-car then pulled up quickly and took up an orbit close by. The colonel had meanwhile instructed the Dak to take off and make for the area.

The four-man stick dropped off by G-one were making their way to the top of the gomo, and a short time later they informed us, "This gomo's clean."

G-one came in quickly to pick them up. Meanwhile we were still in orbit above the scene, trying to figure out where the terrs were hiding. We soon found out.

A Fire Force stick stops for a water-replen. The FN FALs were more accurate and powerful than the terrorists' AKs and SKSs, but they were heavy, and full auto was impossible to control.

The team enjoying some R&R in Salisbury before moving up to Plumtree on the Botswanan border. The camouflage T-shirts and shorts were also worn on operations.

INTELLIGENCE OPERATIONS IN THE BUSH

PRINCIPLES OF ACTION

You are not going to win the war if you erode support for the government by offensive action against innocent villagers or if you fail to protect them from the guerrillas. In both situations the sources of information on which you base your operations will dry up. Military operations must be governed by certain principles:

1. Justification
Every individual operation or military act must be justified and justifiable.

2. Prevention
Your action must be designed to prevent guerrilla activity and illegal acts; it must not be simply an act of revenge or punishment.

3. Minimum force
You must use the minimum force necessary to complete the immediate task at hand.

Because the rural terrorist can so easily merge with the population – he or she may even be part of the local community – an intensive intelligence effort is essential. In Rhodesia, several organisations were involved in the specialised profession of intelligence gathering. The Army also had the Selous Scouts, a multi-racial unit whose speciality involved the infiltration of terrorist networks, as well as the more mundane – but vital – task of mounting long term Observation Posts (OPs).

Obviously, the local population is an ideal source of information, but unless you can gain the trust, confidence and respect of the people the chances of success are greatly reduced. The terrorist will also attempt to win over the locals, for without the supplies, shelter and information provided by the community, he cannot function.

Knowing this, the enemy will make every effort to gain local "support". Initially, he may emulate the methods employed by the Security Forces. However, should diplomacy fail, violence will probably prevail. Why should a terrorist spend months negotiating with a village headman when a

Observation posts were one of main sources of intelligence on guerrilla activity. Unfortunately they are labour intensive, as many days' work may produce nothing of intelligence value unless the enemy happen to be in the right place at the right time. This OP was sited to overlook approaches to a village in the Waffa Waffa region of Rhodesia near Kovelia.

"I resigned from Zanla's war. "Now I'm working for peace with the people and the Pfumo reVanhu."

, DETACHMENT COMMANDER OF ZANLA

"I am ███████ ████, a veteran detachment Commander of the Zanla Forces since 1972. Last year (1978) I was sent to Zimbabwe on operations against the Interim Government Forces in the Msana.
I found the people of Msana happy and contented. I learned that the Forces controlling the area were the forces of the people of Msana (Pfumo reVanhu). I learned that the people of Msana supported the One-Man, One-Vote elections.
I found also that the people of Msana were calling for an end to Nhondo.
I could not go against the wishes of the masses, for the liberation of the masses is what I always believed to be my mission. Now peace is what the people want.
And so I joined the forces of the people of Msana, and I carry my same weapon to help bring peace to Zimbabwe.
Join me, my brothers. The reward is great."

FORWARD WITH PEACE FOR THE PEOPLE. THAT IS WHAT THE PEOPLE WANT.

The aim in Rhodesia was to win the 'hearts and minds' of the population. A guerrilla army cannot be defeated by military means alone: you have to be able to isolate the terrorist from the host population with the minimum amount of damage to innocent parties. The Rhodesian security forces recognised the importance of winning the propaganda battle, and maximum use was made of any enemy they managed to turn round, in this case a ZANLA detachment commander. These leaflets were air dropped.

Combat Skills

bullet in the head will instantly convince his people of the terrorist's cause?

What can you, the man on the ground, do in this complex game? A village subjected to a successful "hearts and minds" campaign will, in theory, respond by co-operating with the Security Forces. However, when a village has been intimidated by a short, violent visit from the local terrorist unit, and provided shelter for the group that then accounts for one or more of your mates, it becomes extremely difficult to feel sympathetic!

Out of the mouths of babes

In such a situation you rarely have the time or the inclination to lecture a kraal's inhabitants on the error of their ways. You must quickly find out all you can about the unit, track it down and wipe it out.

Cold-blooded it may seem, but children are often the ideal source of information. Take a small child to one side and ask a few gentle questions. Has the youngster seen strange people in his village? People with guns like your own? Perhaps a bar of ration-

Questioning adults
Always separate parents and chidren for questioning purposes. Remember, any heavy handed acts could result in the guerrillas gaining a few new recruits or a safe haven in the village.

Hearts and minds
The guerrillas will try to provoke the security forces into committing acts of violence against the community from which they hope to draw support. In this case a patrol has taken sniper fire from a village and has burned two houses in return. Such acts can be counter productive as this may just add weight to the guerrillas' message.

GATHERING INTELLIGENCE

In any guerrilla war the main problem is sorting out who is an enemy and who is an innocent civilian. In the early part of the war in Rhodesia both ZANLA and ZIPRA recruited their freedom fighters by such methods as cordoning off a village and rounding up all the men and boys capable of military service and taking them at gun point across the border to be trained and indoctrinated. These trainees were then sent back into Rhodesia in groups led by hard liners. This policy, which was only abandoned late in the campaign, meant that it was very difficult to define who was a 'Terr'. Accurate and timely intelligence meant that the security forces could isolate the guerrilla from the host community.

Counter moves
The use of terror tactics by the guerrillas is a major factor in intelligence gathering at platoon and company level. They will murder, torture or intimidate the neutral or friendly elements in the local population as they are the most important source of information. It is your job to protect them and thereby convince the population that the 'terrs' will be defeated.

pack chocolate will jog his memory. If he remembers seeing armed men, does he recall when they left his village, and the route they took?

While you are questioning the child, another group can interrogate the concerned parents. Use their fear as a means to an end. For you, the soldier, this could well result in a successful follow-up operation.

Coercion
In the early phases of the war the guerrillas made the mistake of attempting to force the people to support them by executions and other atrocities. Although this achieved some short term goals it severely damaged their efforts to re-educate the people to support the "fight for freedom" which was eventually successful. Later in the war political officers succeeded in convincing the majority and coercion was no longer necessary.

Questioning children
Young children will not usually understand the nature of the war and if you frame your questions carefully and make it a game with incentives such as ration pack sweets you may extract some useful information. Note that information gathered in this way is inherently unreliable.

Specialists
There are a number of specialised organisations involved both in the gathering and assessment of information. You will primarily be concerned with the police and police special branch equivalents, who will have all the background information you need to make sense of the information you receive and put it into context.

NICHOLAS CRABB

A fire force team pose with a 'floppy' or 'gook', as ZANLA or ZIPRA members were known by the security forces. Prisoners are an excellent source of intelligence, but they must be correctly handled to extract accurate information.

Interrogated immediately after capture, this guerrilla led the patrol to where he had hidden the bipod legs for a Russian M1937 mortar, which he is carrying in his handcuffed hands.

A second guerrilla retrieves the base plate for the same mortar, buried nearby. Immediately after capture prisoners are usually suffering from 'shock of capture'; this is when you should try and extract information from them.

Counter-intelligence

The counter-intelligence expert will make a specialist contribution to military security. But his success rate will depend upon the efficiency, alertness and common sense of you, the soldier.

The World War II slogan "Careless talk costs lives" is equally true today. Do not discuss your work and other security matters where you can be overheard by unauthorised persons. This includes bars, restaurants and other public places, even the mess. Classified subjects should not be discussed on the telephone or radio, or with wives, relatives or friends.

Common sense also dictates that you must take due care not to warn the enemy of an impending operation. Yet the stupid mistakes made by some individuals defy belief. In southern Africa it is not unusual for African "batmen" to be employed by officers and troops alike. On one occasion, a commanding officer decided to deploy his men around a small mining town after Intelligence indicated that it had been singled out for a night attack.

Waste of time

To the amazement of the troops involved, they were moved into position at dusk, in full view of their inquisitive batmen. Some of them were soon observed to leave – ostensibly for a night on the town. The operation carried on regardless – and a disgruntled unit spent a freezing cold night on permanent stand-to for nothing! As the troops had foreseen, the batmen had passed news of the ambush around.

Guide to interrogation

You have just fought your way through hellishly dense bush, had two men killed, and faced death yourself. Suddenly, a figure pops up from the undergrowth, tosses aside an AKM and raises his hands in surrender. What do you do?

If you have time to think about it, the chances are you have been lumbered with a prisoner. Now, he must be quickly searched and relieved of equipment before being briefly interrogated.

Limit your questions to those factors affecting the immediate tactical situation. For example:

1 Prisoner's identification
2 Number of those in his group, and their whereabouts
3 Weapons and equipment carried by his unit
4 Clothing worn by his comrades
5 Where the prisoner had come from, and the time he left
6 Prisoner's objective

ZANLA WEAPONS CACHE

This haul of guerrilla weapons was captured on a cross border raid into Mozambique, code named Monte Casino. Note that all the weapons are of Russian manufacture and all are World War II vintage. The rifles are a mixture of bolt action Mosin-Nagant model 1891-30 rifles and model 1938 carbines. Both models have five round box magazines and fire the 7.62 mm Russian rimmed cartridge, which is still in use in the SVD sniper rifle. The rifle has a bayonet that folds flat against the handguard. The machine gun is a 7.62 mm×54 Russian Degtyerev DP model 1928. This is a simple and robust weapon which has a cyclic rate of fire around 600 rounds per minute and is fed with a 47 round pan magazine, examples of which litter the picture. The smaller circular magazines belong to the PPSh-41 sub machine guns, which fire the powerful 7.62 mm bottleneck cartridge. The bolt action rifles may not be much good in a fire fight with the security forces, but the automatic weapons are effective in spite of their age, and in a guerrilla army, where training time is short, simple weapons such as these are ideal for the initial phase of a guerrilla war, where direct confrontation with the security forces will be avoided and the guerrilla will mainly be engaged in terrorising an unarmed population into submission. ZANLA and ZIPRA solved their supply problems as the Bush war escalated and the SKS and AK-47 became their standard rifles. Supplies of PK, RPK and RPD machine guns, rifle grenades, mines, explosives, RPG-7s and even SAM 7 surface to air missiles were carried by patrols operating in Rhodesia. In the later stages of the war, the guerrillas had similar firepower to the security forces looking for them on the ground. However, they never overcame the problem of the Security Forces' air superiority.

7 Terrorist camps or resting places in the area

8 Terrorist supply dumps or caches in the area

9 Terrorist routs and RVs

Obviously, the best time to question a prisoner is immediately after his capture, when he will usually be frightened and shocked. Take advantage of this.

Bang to rights

"Sometimes it is necessary to interrogate a terr in the bush, immediately following his capture. I recall an occasion when we knew that a couple of prisoners had to be terrs who had stashed their kit before being caught. They denied it, of course. However, they had been found in a hut, which had caught fire, and as they were swearing their innocence the bloody hut exploded! They had hidden their ammunition in its thatched roof!

"Interrogating terrs can be a frustrating experience. The African will often tell you what he thinks you want to hear. You have to be very careful how you express a question. Obviously, it's a great help to have among you someone who speaks their language — then a prisoner can't feign ignorance and pretend he doesn't understand".

After questioning, blindfold the captive and tie him up, (if he isn't already), and keep him isolated from other prisoners. Make sure that he does not overhear conversations that could have a bearing on the operation and, when the situation allows, hand him over to the appropriate authorities.

Above: A slightly more ambitious cross border raid by South African troops into Angola produced an impressive haul of Russian supplied armour including T-34/85 tanks, BRDM armoured cars and PT-76 light tanks.

Below: Rhodesian Light Infantry troopies have a quiet word with a guerrilla captured after a brief fire fight. Although the 'terrs' were not afforded the protection of the Geneva convention, mistreatment of prisoners is usually counter productive.

RLI members were thoroughly trained on the full range of Warsaw Pact weapons, many of which were carried as personal weapons. The RPG-7 is certainly a better weapon than the 66mm LAW and as many were captured they became a very popular addition to a patrol's armoury.

The RPG has a considerable backblast, which tends to give away the position of the firer. The weapon does have its uses as an anti-personnel weapon in addition to anti-armour. A common terrorist anti-ambush tactic is to volley fire RPGs back at the ambush position; this tactic worked equally well for the security forces.

Combat Report
Rhodesia:
Guerrilla Contact in the Bush War Part 2

A gunner with the Rhodesian Air Force continues his story of a terrorist contact in the bush war.

"G-one taking flak," came over the radio from G-one's pilot. The terrs had been unable to restrain themselves any longer and had opened up on G-one as he went in to pick up the troops. The browns hit the deck and G-one pulled away quickly, leaving them to make the best of it. G-one was transmitting quite matter-of-factly, "Their fire is coming from my nine o'clock. I think my tech is hit; we've taken a lot of flak." Sure enough, we could see G-one's tech slumped over his guns.

"G-one, make for Landtail," said the colonel.

"Roger, nine."

G-one's nine o'clock had been a neighbouring gomo, the top about half a mile away but with ledges that were considerably closer. Now we knew where they were, and G-one's fate had sharpened our resolve. The colonel called in the Dak while we took up orbit around the southern end of the gomo.

"OK, Joe, put down some rounds, starting on the lowest ledge, working your way slowly upwards."

I took aim and fired short bursts, no more than three rounds at a time; any more would have pushed the chopper sideways and meant us losing our orbit. Then I saw slight movement below, and once my eyes had focussed onto it I picked out first one terr, then another, until I eventually had a number of them in sight.

I will drop smoke

I put some short bursts in among them, picking my targets one at a time and avoiding the temptation to try to hit them all at once, making the most of this first opportunity as I surely wouldn't be presented with a target like this again. Sure enough, after my third or fourth burst a small group broke cover and scuttled off along the side of the gomo.

I let loose round after round, barely pausing between bursts, trying to saturate the whole end of the gomo and bringing down two of the fleeing terrs until the pilot's voice on the intercom gradually penetrated and I settled down again, taking my time. Those terrs who had found cover had been returning our fire but had yet to inflict any damage.

The colonel spoke to the Dak. "Dreadnought, drop your sticks on the open ground to the north of the contact gomo."

"Nine, dreadnought. I have you visual. You are orbiting two gomos; which one is the contact gomo?"

"Stand by, dreadnought. I will drop smoke. G-two, nine. Drop smoke for dreadnought."

"Roger, nine."

G-two was already on his way, and a short time later a rapidly expanding cloud of orange smoke appeared on the ground.

"Dreadnought, nine. Make your drop to the north of the smoke."

"North of the smoke, roger."

The paradrop

As well as identifying the LZ, the smoke gave the Dak pilot the wind strength and direction. The Dak approached the drop zone at 500 ft, a long, straight, slow run, and soon that part of the sky was full of open chutes.

Meanwhile I was still raking the lower part of the gomo with 20-mm rounds. By now I was having as much difficulty scoring any hits as they were; the terrain was providing the terrs with excellent cover. But this soon changed.

The terrs had seen the paradrop, even though it was on their blind side. They broke cover and headed for what they saw as their escape route, the eastern side of the gomo. Their progress along the side of the gomo was quite rapid, considering the terrain, but still they did not present any easy targets. I was able to impede their progress by firing ahead of them and slowly bringing my bursts back towards them, and one or two went down, but not from direct hits, I thought: more likely from shrapnel and ricochets.

By now the terrs were scattered all over the gomo, singly and in small groups, alternately running and stopping to exchange fire with us and the advancing troops. They carried small arms; all seemed to be AK-47s. They were dressed in identical camouflage uniforms, which was unusual, and seemed to be well trained and disciplined, each group trying to provide cover for the next.

I had one group pinned down

We were hoping to catch them as they came off the gomo onto open ground, but there was no guarantee of this as the gomos were grouped closely together and the terrs were bombshelling, splitting up into small groups and heading in different directions, hoping to regroup later. I had one small group pinned down so that if they attempted to escape they would have been torn apart by 20-mm shells.

The paras were now in contact with most of the terrs and soon overran the lot that I was keeping pinned down, disarming and handcuffing them. K-car now took up orbit above the eastern end of the gomo to cut off this means of escape. The rest of the contact was a series of isolated firefights, with the paras gradually gaining the upper hand.

G-two was busy deploying troops and picking up prisoners, who were whisked backed to Landtail. As he touched down in one LZ a group of four terrs appeared in the gunner's sights. He pulled the triggers of the twin Brownings – no need to aim, they were so close – and nothing happened. The terrs had only to raise their weapons and G-two plus occupants would have been history, but they simply turned and ran. Martin, the gunner, was sure he hadn't left the safety catches on, but we'll never know.

G-one rejoined the scene a short while later. His gunner was in a bad way; an AK round had glanced off his flak vest and been directed into his left eye. Landtail had patched him up as best they could, and G-one had flown him back to base at Plumtree, where the returning Dak had picked him up and flown him to hospital in Bulawayo. Meanwhile the Dak ground tech was acting as G-one's gunner.

With G-one back on the scene, we sent G-two off to refuel, and on his return we too made for Landtail and took on fuel and ammo.

Dropped from a Dakota at 500 feet. Low-level drops put paratroopers on the ground at lightning speed, although with increased chances of injury.

We flew back to the contact area and orbited the gomos. The paras had several prisoners, and there were some dead and wounded. The G-cars were now busy picking up wounded troops as well as prisoners and parachutes and transferring everything back to Landtail.

We kept orbiting the area

The troops had formed themselves into four-man sticks and were searching for signs of any remaining terrs, occasionally calling in K-car to sweep the broken terrain with 20-mm rounds – a task we performed with pleasure, for it saved the browns the job of walking into a possible ambush. As the four-man sticks gradually moved away from the contact area, it would become the task of the G-cars to keep them supplied. We would keep orbiting the area in K-car until we were as sure as we could be that there were no more terrs to be accounted for.

As operations went, it hadn't been too bad: finding a number of terrs together before they had a chance to murder any more innocent victims of the bush war, and not too many cock-ups on our behalf.

When the G-cars were at treetop height the crew were in serious danger from enemy small-arms fire. During this engagement one round was deflected by a flak vest and hit the door gunner's eye.

BUSH PATROLLING

The infantry is responsible for a variety of tasks in anti-terrorist operations — for example, you could end up guarding a base deep inside the bush, or perhaps find yourself in a lonely OP overlooking a suspect kraal. Your main task however, is likely to involve hours, days or even weeks on foot patrol. The ability to carry out skilful patrolling that will result in a contact and the elimination of terrorists is the prime task of troops engaged in rural operations.

In the bush, a patrol can consist of anything from four men, up to section and platoon strength. Wherever possible, your commander will be given the limit and boundaries of the patrol area, thereby minimising the risk of patrol clashes. You must obtain clearance if your patrol needs to cross any unit or sub-unit boundaries during an operation.

The knowledge

All patrols must be sent out with a clearly defined mission. Each man should be carefully and thoroughly briefed on the topography, enemy and friendly forces, and local population. The most suitable formation for many types of operation is the four- or five-man patrol pattern, with a centrally placed command group. Distances between groups will depend on the terrain. But they should be sufficiently spread out to prevent an ambush of the entire unit, while being close enough for each group to provide supporting fire in the event of a contact. Distances between individuals will vary according to visibility.

Training for rural operations

There are three basic requirements that are essential for success in bush patrolling.

1 Physical fitness
The terrorist is usually extremely fit and will be travelling light in comparison with the forces tracking him. All troops must therefore be brought up to an exceptional standard of physical fitness through road and cross country running.

2 Marksmanship
In rural operations the soldier needs to fire fast accurate shots at moving targets under 100 m from the standing or kneeling position by day or night.

3 Fieldcraft
The terrorist has naturally good field craft; the bush is his home. Every soldier must reach a similarly high standard in fieldcraft.

A member of the South African 32 Battalion trudges through marshland during the wet season, carrying an AKM assault rifle. As this is a cross border raid he carries a very large external frame rucksack to support the huge load of equipment required 'on externals'.

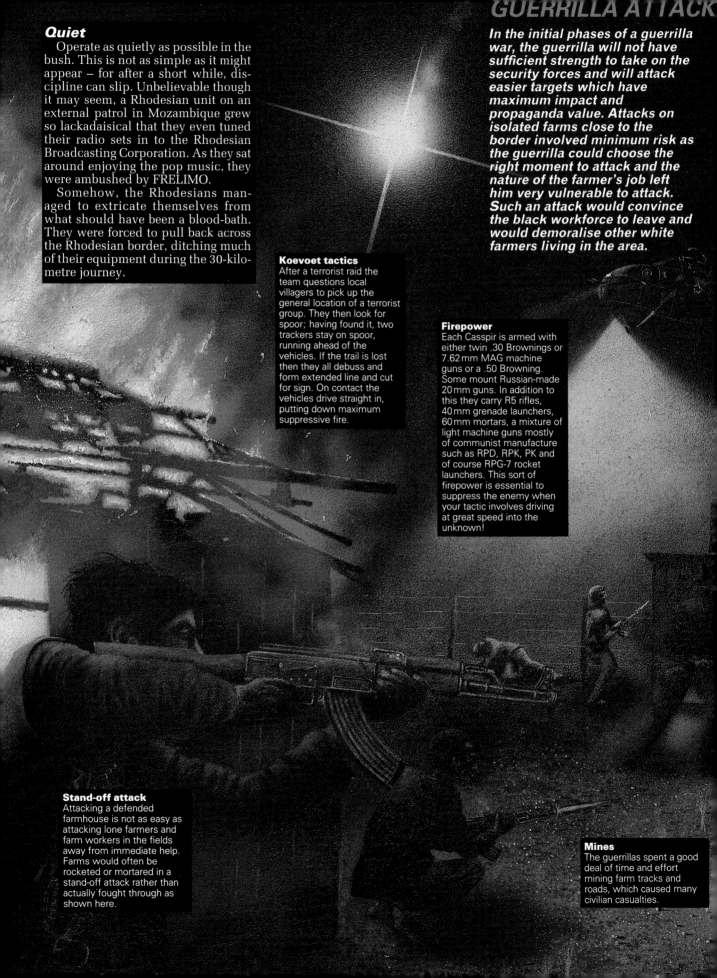

Quiet

Operate as quietly as possible in the bush. This is not as simple as it might appear – for after a short while, discipline can slip. Unbelievable though it may seem, a Rhodesian unit on an external patrol in Mozambique grew so lackadaisical that they even tuned their radio sets in to the Rhodesian Broadcasting Corporation. As they sat around enjoying the pop music, they were ambushed by FRELIMO.

Somehow, the Rhodesians managed to extricate themselves from what should have been a blood-bath. They were forced to pull back across the Rhodesian border, ditching much of their equipment during the 30-kilometre journey.

In the initial phases of a guerrilla war, the guerrilla will not have sufficient strength to take on the security forces and will attack easier targets which have maximum impact and propaganda value. Attacks on isolated farms close to the border involved minimum risk as the guerrilla could choose the right moment to attack and the nature of the farmer's job left him very vulnerable to attack. Such an attack would convince the black workforce to leave and would demoralise other white farmers living in the area.

Koevoet tactics

After a terrorist raid the team questions local villagers to pick up the general location of a terrorist group. They then look for spoor; having found it, two trackers stay on spoor, running ahead of the vehicles. If the trail is lost then they all debuss and form extended line and cut for sign. On contact the vehicles drive straight in, putting down maximum suppressive fire.

Firepower

Each Casspir is armed with either twin .30 Brownings or 7.62 mm MAG machine guns or a .50 Browning. Some mount Russian-made 20 mm guns. In addition to this they carry R5 rifles, 40 mm grenade launchers, 60 mm mortars, a mixture of light machine guns mostly of communist manufacture such as RPD, RPK, PK and of course RPG-7 rocket launchers. This sort of firepower is essential to suppress the enemy when your tactic involves driving at great speed into the unknown!

Stand-off attack

Attacking a defended farmhouse is not as easy as attacking lone farmers and farm workers in the fields away from immediate help. Farms would often be rocketed or mortared in a stand-off attack rather than actually fought through as shown here.

Mines

The guerrillas spent a good deal of time and effort mining farm tracks and roads, which caused many civilian casualties.

Another precaution against ambush is to avoid making obvious tracks. The Rhodesians hit upon an idea that worked for a while. They began to issue "clandestine" boots, without a recognisable tread. However, before long the enemy realised that only the security forces wore the smooth-soled footwear! It was far more practical to wear boots and shoes with soles identical to those used by the terrorists – a tactic soon adopted by many Rhodesians.

Walk into it

There are of course several methods of patrolling, and experience counts for a lot in the bush. You will soon learn that in Africa it isn't always necessary – or practical – to move at a cautious pace. In Rhodesia, the accepted style was to remain upright and simply walk forward until contact was initiated.

In especially thick bush however, it isn't always practical to look through the dense foliage at head height. Although it is uncomfortable to shuffle along in a crouched position, you can often see far more in especially thick bush by peering through the thinner undergrowth close to the ground.

Contact, when it occurs, is almost always sudden, short and unexpected. Your response will depend on the circumstances. If you see the enemy first, you should react with an immediate ambush. If you see each other simultaneously, take immediate offensive action. Should the enemy

Farm security
Many farms were comprehensively fortified and equipped with intruder alarm systems and mobile patrols from private security companies in addition to regular army and police patrols.

Inherited expertise
Lessons learned by the Rhodesians were passed on to the South Africans as many members of elite units such as the Selous scouts saw very little future in staying in Zimbabwe and emigrated, in some cases with their equipment and weapons. The South Africans have learned that there is no value in deploying all-white units and indigenous troops are employed in large numbers to provide trackers.

Follow-up
Follow-up usually involved many careful hours of patrolling, with tracking teams examining spoor and stop groups being placed out by helicopter to cut off the enemy retreat. These operations can be extremely hazardous as you could be tracking your way into an enemy ambush and a Casspir or Ratel will not protect you from RPG rockets.

Communications
Most farmers on isolated farms were equipped with radio in addition to the telephone. Such measures meant that a quick reaction force could be on the scene very quickly, but catching the enemy in this situation is unlikely.

Counter terrorist operations
In response to this type of attack by SWAPO on white farmers in Namibia, the South Africans deployed the Koevoet or the South West African Police Counter Insurgency Division in preference to the regular army. The Koevoet basic operational unit was a hunter killer team made up of 40 Ovambo trackers led by four white officers or NCOs mounted in four Casspir armoured cars and one Blesbok supply vehicle.

A patrol stop for a water replen. Remember that a water supply such as this mucky pool may be the only water source for miles around, so you and the enemy will both have to use it: obviously a good spot for an ambush. Note the chest webbing rig worn by the soldier squatting in the foreground.

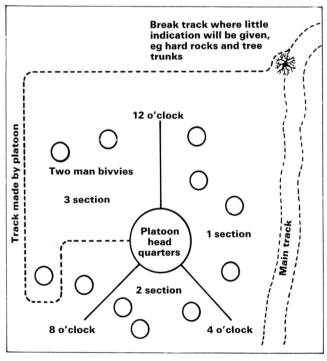

A South African patrol on internal security operations prepare for redeployment by Puma. The helicopter allows a small force to dominate a far larger patrol area than would be possible on foot alone. The South Africans do not suffer from the equipment shortages that dogged the Rhodesian security forces.

sight you first, take immediate offensive action as you would in reacting to an ambush.

Shoot back fast

Instant aggressive action is the key to success in the bush. The one time you are likely to be in serious trouble is when on the receiving end of an ambush. However, the average African terrorist will not stand his ground if you return effective fire.

During an ambush in Angola in 1980, a group from South Africa's 32 Battalion were pinned down for 20 minutes by a large FAPLA force. Eventually, the South Africans launched a desperate frontal attack against their aggressors. FAPLA broke and ran, leaving behind six dead. The

South Africans lost one killed and 22 wounded. The outcome could have been far worse for the South Africans, but for their determined and aggressive spirit.

Well-trained and hardened troops can make a base practically anywhere. The case of the musical patrol ambushed in Mozambique clearly demonstrates the necessity of taking

PATROL FORMATIONS

Formation 1
Direction of movement ↑
Thick bush

Formation 2
Direction of movement ↑
Open grassland

Formation 3
Direction of movement ↑
Thick bush

○ Command group
▬ Fire team
T Tracker

Patrol formation is usually dictated by the ground and the enemy threat. Each team has 4 men including a MAG gunner and a radio operator. Formation 1 is vulnerable to fire from the front but can be quickly redeployed into assault formation shown in formation 2. Formation 3 provides good all round protection.

TEMPORARY PLATOON BASE

Break track where little indication will be given, eg hard rocks and tree trunks

Track made by platoon

12 o'clock

Two man bivvies

3 section

Platoon head quarters

1 section

Main track

2 section

8 o'clock

4 o'clock

The platoon harbour is used as a secure base from which to launch operations such as section level OPs and ambushes or as a base for rest and administration. This layout means that 1 section would cover the main track and 3 section would put a sentry out to cover the trail the platoon had left leading into the harbour position.

On contact the terrs had the option to stand and fight, withdraw en masse or bomb-burst and exfiltrate in twos or threes. The first two options usually provide a good target for a 'frantan' (napalm) attack delivered by a Cessna 327 Lynx. Air support certainly gave the security forces the edge over the guerrillas in the Bush war.

'Grazing' time in the bush. The chef in this patrol harbour has built a rock fire place to prevent the fire spreading and has a brew going in one metal mug whilst cooking food in another.

care after moving into an area. Take care over siting a base. Some problems are unique to Africa.

For instance, when the scarcity of water dictates that you lie up close to the only water for miles around, you should bear in mind that any terrorists in the vicinity will also need to replenish their water supply from the same source. Game tracks should be avoided. If wild animals scent humans, they will probably leave the track and create a new one, thus indicating your presence to a watchful enemy.

An efficient base is essentially one in which:

1 Security arrangements are sound and known to all
2 Duties are evenly distributed and rest is organised
3 Strict hygiene rules and water discipline are laid down and observed
4 A high all-round standard of discipline is maintained.

Follow-up

The aim of the follow-up, or pursuit, is to track down, attack and destroy an enemy group that may or may not have had contact with the security forces.

During daylight, the follow-up unit should be supported by a light aircraft, which should be armed if the tracks are relatively fresh (less than 48 hours old). Where tracks are several days old, troops can be helicoptered forward in order to find more recent spoor. Place stop groups forward, astride the estimated line of advance.

As soon as possible after the follow-up begins, send an additional force back-tracking from the start point to ensure that no enemy have

stayed behind. This group can also search for any hides and resting places and recover abandoned enemy material.

When contact is imminent, helicopters should be made available to the unit. This by now will have broken down into sticks. Immediately after contact, search the area thoroughly for enemy casualties, abandoned equipment, spoor of escaping terrorists, and for secondary hides and RVs.

Tracking

In difficult terrain, the security forces will often use an African tracker, whose proficiency can be truly astounding.

"I was involved in an op where we were to mount an OP on a hill near a suspect kraal. From the very beginning, our tracker insisted we were wasting our time. He had deduced

that there had been a number of terrs in the vicinity, but they had departed two or three days previously. He showed us where they had paused to rest and the direction they had then gone. Nevertheless, we carried on with the OP. After about three days we pulled out. Before leaving though, we talked to the villagers. They confirmed all that our tracker had said."

Because local trackers are easily available, usually only specialist troops tend to be taught the art. You may pick up a few points during the course of your service, but real tracking takes many months, even years, of practical experience.

South African artillery is probably the most modern in the world but, like the Soviets, they never throw anything away and that includes museum pieces such as this 5.5 inch howitzer. In Africa any gun is better than no gun at all.

RELOADING DRILLS

There are many weird and wonderful ways of carrying magazines, such as assault vests and chest pouches. While these may look the business for posing on the streets of Beirut, they are a hindrance to accurate shooting from the prone position because the magazines stick in your ribs. For this reason, it is advisable to keep your conventional belt magazine pouches positioned on your hips.

The commonest stoppage is an empty magazine. Weapons with automatic hold-open devices will lock the bolt to the rear effectively, telling you that you have fired the last shot. With practice you can dump the empty, palm in a fresh mag and hit the bolt release to chamber the first round in three seconds. You must practise this in all positions, including prone.

Bolt action technique

Bolt-action rifles are still widely used for sniping. Correct bolt-action technique is to keep the rifle in your shoulder with your left hand. Watch the target while moving your head slightly back off the stock as your right hand works the bolt to chamber the next round, without losing your sight picture.

Stripper clips

There is a limit to how many magazines you can effectively carry; reloading magazines is time-consuming. Most 5.56-mm and 7.62-mm weapons have stripper clip systems for quick reloading. 5.56-mm is usually issued in bandoliers of 100 rounds in 10-round stripper clips. 7.62-mm can still be obtained in bandoliers of 50 in five-round clips.

Carrying ammunition

Chest webbing does have its place if you are likely to be firing while standing or kneeling. It is also useful in fighting in built-up areas, where pouches on your hips could make movement in enclosed spaces difficult.

Your system of ammunition carriage must be purpose-built for your weapon. This system is compatible with SA80: each pouch is designed for two 30-round mags of 5.56-mm and nothing else.

The correct loading position

Hold the rifle by the pistol grip with your right hand, your forefinger outside the trigger guard and the muzzle pointed upwards. Check that the safety catch is applied, unfasten your magazine pouch, and tilt the rifle slightly to the strong side. Take the magazine from the pouch and insert it in your rifle, making sure that it locks in properly.

Speed reloading

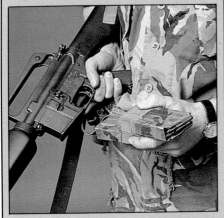

You can speed up your reload time by taping mags end-to-end like this, but it ruins the balance of the weapon and you could damage or get dirt in the bottom mag. This technique can be appropriate in FIBUA or night patrols. Alternatively you can load all your mags with a tracer round third from bottom. When you see that go, you know you can fire one more shot and then you need to change mags, leaving one round in the chamber: all you have to do is simply change magazines and carry on firing.

Reload drill

1 Most people cannot count to 20 when being shot at, so when the weapon stops firing cock, hook and look in the usual way, remove the empty and drop it down the front of your combat jacket.

2 Shout 'magazine change' to your partner and get into cover. Leave the working parts to the rear and the safety catch off, and reach for the fresh mag with your left hand.

3 Clip the magazine firmly into place and check it, then close the pouch before you move. Also, organise your ammunition carriage so that there is no way you can reload with an empty or half-expended magazine.

4 As soon as the fresh mag is on, pull back on the cocking handle. You must be able to do this automatically without having to look: you will need to concentrate on what the enemy and your skirmishing partner are up to.

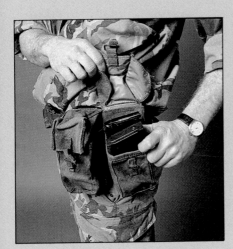

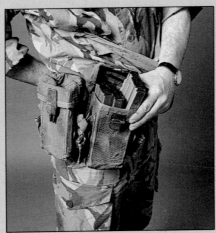

A better system is to have your magazines in individual pouches on your left side, and leave the right side for grenades. This is the Soviet system and it obviously works well enough for the SAS, who use this four-magazine pouch, with high and low belt loops.

You must be able to open and close a pouch quickly under stress. The US ALICE system has a push-close locking pouch designed to take three 30-round M16 mags. The system works well, and grenades can be fitted each side of the pouch in individual pockets.

The system you choose must be robust. The British 58 pattern is poor in all respects but this. It is difficult to close, and has to be padded so that you can grip the mags easily and so that they do not rattle. It seems to be designed for three and a half 20-round SLR mags.

USING SIGHTS, SLINGS AND BIPODS

There are many assault rifle accessories on the market, but none of them will be right for every job. For instance, high-powered telescopic sights are fine for a sniper but will limit your field of view and can be a hindrance at short range. When you have mastered the basics, experiment to find the right kit for you and your task.

The right telescopic sight and the addition of a bipod can enhance the grouping capacity of a good shot. They will do nothing for a bad shot except magnify his error.

Using your sling

The carrying sling of your rifle can be a very useful aid to steady your position. It is best used when firing from the prone position and can be employed in two ways.

1 Single point

Form a small loop by doubling back one end of the sling. Pass the opposite end of the sling through the small loop to form a larger free running loop. Fix the end without the loop to the front sling attachment of the rifle and pass your supporting arm through the loop, which is then positioned above the bicep.

Now adopt the prone position and pass your supporting hand outside and over the sling and into position on the handguard. The sling should lie under the back of your hand. Test and adjust your position as normal. It is important that the tension of the sling is correct – take up any slack by adjusting the position of the forward buckle.

2 Combat sling

Attach the sling to the rifle in its normal carrying mode. Adopt your firing position and put your supporting arm through the sling and position above the bicep. Place your left hand under and then over the forward end of the sling, so that when you cradle the handguard it is wrapped under the back of your hand and over the top of your forearm. Test and adjust your position as normal. When the sling is used in this way, tension should be positive but not too tight as this will alter your Mean Point of Impact. Adjust the position of the forward buckle for the correct amount of tension.

The sling can be used to improve the stability of all shooting positions. First adjust the sling to the correct length so that it is comfortable. Make sure you are wearing what you usually shoot in, and be aware that the sling will affect your MPI.

The sling can also be used to carry the weapon in a non-aggressive stance while allowing you to get into a fire position at speed. You should never carry a rifle over your shoulder except where there is no threat.

With the sling adjusted to the right length and placed over your head, you can quickly move into the standing position by punching out, using both arms, to snap the rifle up into the aim. This method of carriage also leaves your hands free to do other tasks.

With a good telescope you can spot a target, identify it and place shots accurately on it at ranges that would not be possible with iron sights. The Nimrod scope fitted to the sniper Galil also has a primitive rangefinder based on the average height of a man.

The scope is not well suited to close-range battle shooting and can be easily damaged. You must choose carefully. Colt produce an excellent scope for the Armalite AR-15-based weapons.

Telescopic sights can be fitted to almost any rifle. This is a Kar 98k fitted with a pistol scope, so that the weapon can still be clip loaded. However, think long and hard about fitting a system that leaves you with no sights if the scope fails. On any battle rifle you should be able to use the iron sights in an emergency.

Left: Close-quarter battle is where the single-point red dot sights come into their own. At close range they provide very rapid target acquisition. Using both eyes open, the red aiming dot appears in the same optical plane as the target.

Above: The alternatives are roll-on, roll-off mounts so that the scope is easily removed without spoiling the zero or (in the case of this FAL) fitting the scope to a spare top cover.

Use of bipod

Some modern assault rifles, such as the Galil, are fitted with a bipod, and the Parker Hale M.85 sniper rifle and Accuracy's new L96 for the British Army all have bipods as standard kit. The bipod is simple to use and an effective aid to steadying the firing position.

Adopt the standard prone position, but place your body directly in line with the rifle instead of being at an angle. Your feet should be spread further apart than they would be in standard prone. There are many variations on the placement of the supporting hand – the easiest and most effective is the crossed arm hold with the left hand supporting the bottom of the butt. You then control elevation by moving your elbows closer together or further apart.

When using the bipod, make sure that its legs are securely positioned in the ground because you need to exert forward force when aiming and firing. Ensure that the butt of the rifle is kept firmly positioned in the shoulder at all times.

Alternatively, you can carry the rifle with your head and shoulder through the sling so that the rifle is across your chest. From this position you can quickly bring the rifle up into the underarm assault position.

There are many different types of bipod available and some assault rifles like the Galil have them built in. Note the firing position with the thumb hooked through the folding stock. The LSW has an extra handle on the butt for use when firing from the tripod.

Bipods enhance stability and accuracy when firing from defensive positions, but bipods clipped onto the barrel, such as this M16 bipod, will push your MPI up several centimetres at 100 metres. If you do not allow for this at longer ranges, you will miss the target.

1285

SAFE HANDLING, LOAD & UNLOAD

The sub-machine-gun is an excellent weapon for close-quarter battle. In street fighting, wood clearing and on patrols it offers unbeatable close-range firepower. However, SMGs make frequent and invariably inaccurate appearances in the cinema, and most soldiers do not get enough live firing experience with them. Consequently, sub-machine-guns are badly misunderstood and have a poor safety record. It is essential that you understand how they work and how to handle them in complete safety.

General characteristics of SMGs

1 Sub-machine-guns usually fire pistol ammunition. The most common calibre is 9-mm Parabellum, but some designs are chambered for .22 LR, .32 ACP, .380 ACP and .45 ACP.

2 Most SMGs have a safety catch with three positions: safe, single-shot and fully automatic fire. Some are only capable of fully automatic fire and some are also fitted with additional safety devices such as grip safety and bolt locking catches.

3 Most sub-machine-guns are direct blowback, open-bolt weapons, although a few are closed-bolt (e.g. the HK MP5).

4 Sights are usually post and aperture or post and notch. They vary from extremely crude fixed types to fully adjustable rifle types. There are some excellent optical and laser sights available.

Safe handling rules

The SMG is a short-barrelled weapon and is easier to point in a dangerous direction than a rifle. The weapon fires from an open bolt, which means that negligent discharges through mishandling are common.

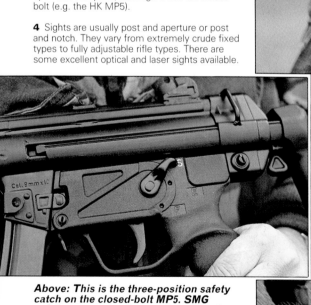

Above: This is the three-position safety catch on the closed-bolt MP5. SMG safety arrangements vary from this, the more conventional layout, to simple slots cut out of the receiver for the bolt or bolts that can be locked by the cocking piece.

*Safe handling with **SMGs** must become instinctive: there are more accidents with this type of weapon than with any other weapon currently in service. The Skorpion clearly demonstrates the problems. **SMGs** are short-barrelled, which makes it easy to muzzle-sweep people, or in this case possibly lose your finger tips! The open-bolt mechanism is also particularly unforgiving.*

Normal safety precautions

You should carry out this drill every time you pick up a weapon, hand it over to another soldier, enter a building or get on a vehicle, at the beginning and end of every weapon training lesson, and when drawing or handing in the weapon at the armoury. If you are in any doubt about the state of a weapon, carry out NSPs. The command to carry out the drill is 'For inspection, port arms'.

1 Hold the weapon by the pistol grip, muzzle pointing upwards or in a safe direction, e.g. downrange. Keep your finger on the trigger guard, not the trigger.

2 Put the safety catch or selector to safe and remove the magazine if fitted.

3 Now set the safety catch to automatic and, with the forefinger and thumb of the left hand, cock the weapon and eyeball the chamber and breech for live rounds. Also look to see if there is a round on the bolt face (unlikely). Wait for the weapon to be inspected at this stage.

4 When ordered to 'ease springs' or 'clear' by the person you are handing the weapon to, take hold of the cocking handle, squeeze the trigger and let the bolt forward under control. Then re-apply the safety catch.

NSPs basically mean a complete unload. First, point the weapon in a safe dirction, put the safety catch at safe, and remove the magazine. NDs often result from soldiers carrying out the unload drill with a magazine fitted.

Next, set the safety catch to 'R' or 'A' and pull back the bolt, eyeball the chamber and then let the working parts forward by holding the bolt with the left hand and squeezing the trigger with the right. Do not pull back on the cocking handle or you will simply re-engage the sear.

The make ready

1 The SMG is normally carried loaded with the safety catch on: in this state it is safe. It is critically important that you realise 'Load' and 'Ready' are two entirely different states. When you are give the order 'Ready', you must first move the safety catch to 'R' for single shots.

Load procedure

1 With the weapon in a safe direction, either the high port load position or weapon downrange, check the safety catch is at safe with your left hand with your trigger finger on the trigger guard, not the trigger.

2 Take a charged magazine from your pouch and check that the top rounds are correctly seated and the magazine lips are not damaged.

Magazine filling

SMG magazines, with the exception of some of the more exotic designs, are all simple box-type mags that are filled in the same way as pistol magazines. The springs are usually a good deal stronger, and getting the last few rounds in can be a problem. Some weapons are issued with mag filling tools, such as this one for the Swedish Carl Gustav.

3 Insert the magazine straight into the magazine well until you hear a click. Then try to remove it to check that the magazine is fully home and locked by the magazine catch. Then close the pouch. The weapon is now described as loaded but not made ready.

2 Use the forefinger and thumb to grip the cocking handle and firmly rack the bolt. You should feel it engage the sear. This is where NDs (Negligent Discharges) may happen. Every time the bolt goes forward it will fire a round if there is ammunition there. Reapply the safety catch unless you are about to fire.

Heckler & Koch: Teutonic Enforcer

Main pic: Firing the Heckler & Koch P9S, a well-built .45 ACP semi-automatic pistol which uses the same roller locking system as the H&K rifles. Intended mainly for the police market, which prizes reliability above all else, the P9S is a robust weapon with no frills.

The West German company of Heckler & Koch produces some of the finest automatic pistols available today. Widely used by police and paramilitary units as well as armies, their range offers something for everyone. The company was founded by two ex-Mauser employees in 1950 when weapons production was permitted again in West Germany. Initially building the G3 rifle in the old Mauser factory at Oberndorf, they soon expanded into the pistol market with the HK4.

The HK4 was highly successful: it could be quickly changed, without using tools, from 9-mm Short to 7.65-mm ACP, to 6.25-mm ACP and finally to .22 Long Rifle. You could buy it in any calibre and, by acquiring the spare barrels, return springs and magazines, convert your gun at will.

Shortly after it was introduced, H&K decided to go after the military and police markets with a 9-mm handgun. By this time the company had perfected the roller-locked delayed blowback system of operation used in the G3 rifle and had adapted it to their sub-machine-gun. Adapting it to a pistol, they produced the P9. In 9-mm Parabellum or 7.65-mm Parabellum chambering, it used the same roller locking system as the H&K rifles, with a two-part bolt locking into a barrel extension.

Above: Polygonal rifling is employed in the P9, which is claimed to boost muzzle velocity and ease maintenance, but whether it copes as well with the wear and tear of factory ammunition is open to doubt.

Right: A security camera in a bank shows H&K pistols doing what they are built for. The robber (left) shoots a policeman (centre) but is shot in turn by another officer (right). The wounded police officer survived because his radio stopped the bullet.

The P9 was followed very quickly by the P9S, the same pistol but with double-action lockwork, and in 1975 H&K announced that they would now make both pistols in .45 ACP calibre for the American market, while the version in 7.65-mm Parabellum would be discontinued since there was little demand for that calibre.

Meanwhile, after the P9 and P9S had been launched, the company did some really original thinking and launched an entirely new pistol concept which, they felt, held great potential. This was the VP70.

The burst-fire VP70

The VP70 was among the first pistols to make extensive use of plastic in its construction, the frame being a steel skeleton clad in plastic material. It was also unusual in being a 9-mm Parabellum blowback pistol, relying solely on the weight of the slide and the strength of the return spring to control the action. But the most unusual thing about it was that it was provided with a removable shoulder stock, also of plastic. When this stock was clipped into place on the rear of the pistol, a tongue slid into the lockwork of the VP70 and turned it into a machine pistol capable of firing a three-round burst for every pressure on the trigger.

The idea of putting a shoulder stock on a pistol was far from new; the idea of a full-auto pistol with a stock was likewise fairly old. But the three-round burst idea was entirely new in the pistol world; it had only recently been tried on assault rifles. Full-auto pistols have a serious defect: when fired, they empty their magazines in about one and a half seconds and the barrel ends up vertical. The blast of fire causes the muzzle to rise com-

Loading a fresh magazine into the P9S: note the adjustable rear sight. Once manufactured in 7.65-mm Parabellum, it is now only available in 9-mm or .45 ACP, although the latter has never really caught on.

When the last round has been fired the slide will lock to the rear. Insert a fresh mag and release it by pressing the cocking lever on the left of the receiver or racking the slide back and letting the return spring drive it forward.

The magazine release catch is located underneath the pistol grip. Push the catch to the rear to extract the magazine. With nine rounds' magazine capacity in 9 mm, the P9 is rather more concealable than chunkier-gripped weapons like the Beretta 92F.

pletely beyond the firer's control As a result, most of the ammunition is wasted. But the three-round burst fired at a rate of 2,200 rounds per minute – the three rounds are gone in .027 of a second – gives the gun muzzle little chance to rise. As a result, the three rounds land fairly close together in the target area.

Lack of interest

You might think that there would have been a rush to H&K's door; but the world proved curiously resistant to the VP70. A number of countries purchased small numbers for evaluation and some minor African countries bought them in some numbers, but it never really took off. Several people complained about its accuracy (though our experience with two gave quite reasonable results), and police forces looked askance at the three-round burst feature. So the VP70Z was introduced; this was the VP70 'Zivil', which did away with the shoulder stock and three-round burst feature, just a plain pistol. This didn't do well either, probably because in the early 1970s people simply could not adjust to the idea of a pistol made largely of plastic.

The new PSP

H&K abandoned production of the VP70 in the early 1980s but they had now come up with a fresh design which really did pull in the customers. In the middle 1970s the West German police were becoming more and more involved in the fight against terrorism, and they decided that they needed a new pistol. A squad of practical policemen sat down to draw up a specification, and their principal points were a large magazine capacity, calibre not less than 9-mm Parabellum, a high standard of safety, and a weapon that could be brought into action with the minimum of delay. Several companies went after this design, since it promised substantial contracts from the various West German state police forces and, of course, from foreign forces who would view West German police approval as being a certificate of merit.

The H&K design appeared as the 'PSP' for 'Polizei selbst-ladener pistole' and, typically, offered some new ideas. In 9-mm Parabellum calibre, it had a 13-round magazine and was a delayed blowback pistol using an unusual gas system to obtain the delay. The barrel is fixed, and beneath it is a cylinder, connected to the barrel by a small port just in front

Field stripping the HK P9S

The Heckler & Koch P9S with some serious factory ammunition. Police pistols must be able to handle powerful factory loads without trouble The weapon has a pin-type loaded chamber indicator at the top rear of the chamber, rather like the Luger.

To field strip the P9, engage the safety, remove the magazine and examine the chamber carefully to check that it is clear. When the weapon is cocked a small steel bar protrudes out of the back of the receiver. The back of this can easily be seen or felt at night.

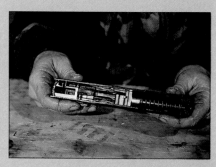

Press the takedown catch, which is in the rear surface of the trigger guard in front of the trigger.

Push the slide as far forward as it will go and pull it off, upwards and forwards.

Push the barrel forward against the return spring until it can be removed. Do not pull the recoil spring off the barrel.

Once disassembled, the bolt-head can be removed by using one side of the barrel extension to press between the bolt-head and the slide against the locking lever until the bolt-head comes forward. You can then remove the bolt.

of the chamber. Attached to the front of the slide is a piston-rod, surrounded by a return spring, which, when the pistol is assembled, enters the front of the gas cylinder under the barrel. On firing, a proportion of the propellant gas leaks into the cylinder; as the slide begins to move back, driven by the gas pressure forcing out the cartridge case, the piston is driven

into the cylinder. But its movement is resisted by the gas pressure, so the opening of the breech is delayed.

The second novelty lies in the firing system. There is no safety catch, but there is a prominent 'squeeze grip' forming the front edge of the butt. As you pick up the pistol you instinctively squeeze this back, and this cocks the firing pin ready for the first

Inside the HK P7

The P7 has been adopted by the West German army as the ultimate replacement for the Walther P1. The P7M13 is a modified version produced for the 1981 US JSSAP tests and is now marketed commercially.

Foresight

Rearsight
Able to be adjusted only for windage, the sights use the three-dot system for swift target acquisition.

Bolt

Striker

Polygonal rifling
This is claimed to reduce fouling and ease maintenance. The gun is designed only for full metal jacket factory ammunition. You can use jacketed bullets but the gun will need very thorough cleaning.

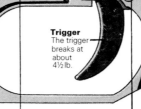

Gas mechanism
Part of the gases produced on firing are diverted through this vent, fractionally delaying the rearward movement of the slide.

Trigger
The trigger breaks at about 4½ lb.

13-round magazine
The M- designation after the P7 refers to magazine capacity: hence the P7M13 carries the 13 rounds specified by the US pistol tests. The M8 carries eight rounds, making for a more concealable gun.

9-mm Parabellum
The gas retarded mechanism is sensitive to pressure curve variations and only really likes full-power factory ammunition. If you are bold enough to hand-load 9-mm rounds, restrict yourself to fast-burning powders and eschew lighter bullets.

Piston
This can only retract when the round has left the barrel and pressure has fallen to a safe level. This then makes the slide recoil and eject the spent case. On the way back it chambers the next round.

Squeeze cocking lever
Unless this is pushed in the trigger cannot be released, so accidental firing is a little harder. It needs about 15-lb pressure to cock the striker but only about 2 lb to hold it cocked.

The P7 is a standard pistol for the West German police and army. Its squeeze cocking device makes it a distinctive gun and it is recognised as a simple, reliable weapon built to high manufacturing standards.

shot. Release your grip and the firing pin is de-cocked and the weapon is safe. Squeeze, and pull the trigger, and the pistol fires. As the slide goes back and reloads, so the firing pin is automatically cocked ready for the next shot – so long as you keep the grip

squeezed. Relax, and you are in the safe condition again. So there is no danger of the pistol accidentally firing should it be dropped, for example.

The PSP is very accurate, and it was soon adopted by a number of state police forces, by the Bundeswehr and

its Special Forces, and then by many police and security forces outside West Germany – even some US police forces are using it. It was rechristened the 'Pistole 7' by the West German police, and so H&K adopted the same nomenclature, producing two

The VP70 weapons system

The VP70 was one of Heckler & Koch's most innovative designs, but a variety of circumstances prevented it achieving popularity and it is no longer manufactured. Fired single-handed, it is a basic semi-automatic pistol which makes considerable use of plastic in its construction. The wide grip holds an 18-round magazine.

When the shoulder stock is fitted, a tongue goes into the lock work so that the VP70 fires a three-round burst for each squeeze of the trigger. The high cyclic rate of fire ensures that the third round has left the muzzle before your aim has been seriously disturbed. The rate of fire imposes massive force on the gun, but the VP70 is claimed to have an operational life of 30,000 rounds plus.

models, the P7M13 and the P7M8, the latter having a magazine holding only eight shots; this made the pistol slightly more compact for those who wanted a concealed weapon.

In 1987 the P7M7 appeared. This is in .45 ACP calibre and the method of obtaining the delayed blowback action has been changed. The piston and cylinder are more or less the same, but in this case the cylinder is not connected to the barrel and is filled with oil, while the piston has a valve system. On firing, the piston forces against the oil, which is incompressible, and can only move under control via the valve, so braking the rearward movement of the slide. This

is similar to the recoil brake used on heavy artillery, and it is entirely novel to see it successfully used on a pistol. The oil buffer not only delays the breech opening but also soaks up a lot of the recoil. This is probably the most controllable .45 pistol ever made.

Newest design

The most recent H&K design is a variant of the P7 system known as the P7PT8. It looks exactly like the standard P7M8 except for a vivid blue spot on the slide and a blue engraving 'PLASTIC TRAINING ONLY'. There are some minor internal differences, due to the fact that it is designed solely to fire 9-mm training ammunition fit-

ted with plastic bullets. Using this ammunition the pistol has a maximum range of about 125 metres, though at that range it would scarcely bruise you. At 8-10 metres' range it is as accurate as the standard pistol using ball ammunition. And it has one more advantage: the plastic bullet deforms when it hits anything hard, but at short range the combination of light weight and high velocity can wound or even kill, and the P7PT8 is being closely studied as a possible anti-hijack weapon for use inside aircraft. It can dispose of a hijacker without endangering the pressurised cabin structure.

Battlefield Evaluation: comparing

Heckler & Koch P7

The prominent squeeze cocking device on the front of the grip cocks the pistol ready for the first shot and, when released, de-cocks the firing pin. There are three versions: the P7M13, with 13 rounds, and the P7M8 with eight rounds, which is easier to conceal. Most interesting is the P7M7, intended for the American market; this is chambered for .45 ACP and uses an artillery style hydraulic recoil system.

Specification:
Cartridge: 9-mm Parabellum
Weight: 850 g (without magazine)
Length: 17.5 cm
Barrel length: 10.5 cm
Magazine: 8 or 13 rounds

Assessment
Reliability ★★★★
Accuracy ★★★★
Age ★★
Worldwide users ★★★

The H&K P7 series has been adopted by the West German army and police forces.

Heckler & Koch P9

The P9 uses the famous Heckler & Koch roller-locked delayed blowback system originally developed for the G3 rifle. The P9 is single action, but the later P9S is double action. The gun is produced in .45 ACP for the American market and was briefly produced in 7.65-mm Parabellum. It is used by West German and many other police forces and military units.

Specification:
Cartridge: 9-mm Parabellum or .45 ACP
Weight: 880 g (magazine empty)
Length: 19.2 cm
Barrel length: 10.2 cm
Magazine: 9 round box (.45 ACP 7 rounds)

Assessment
Reliability ★★★★
Accuracy ★★★
Age ★★★★
Worldwide users ★★★★

The P9 is an interesting double-action delayed-blowback weapon with a number of unique safety features.

VP70

The innovative VP70 is used by a few military and police forces and was widely sold in Asia and Africa, but it never achieved the commercial success it deserved. The military version has a detachable shoulder stock which enables the gun to fire three-round bursts when it is attached. At a cyclic rate of 2200 rounds per minute, the third shot has left the weapon before the recoil seriously affects your aim.

Specification:
Cartridge: 9-mm Parabellum
Weight: 820 g (unloaded)
Length: 20.4 cm
Barrel length: 11.6 cm
Magazine: 18 rounds

Assessment
Reliability ★★★★
Accuracy ★★★★
Age ★★★
Worldwide users ★

The radical VP70 failed to make a significant impact, and is no longer in production.

Left and above: The P9S has a number of interesting built-in features. Firstly, after chambering a round and cocking the weapon you can apply the safety catch and squeeze the trigger to decock the weapon, and then carry it 'hammer down' rather than 'cocked and locked'. You can then either slide the safety off and fire the first shot double-action or press the slide release down firmly, which will recock the weapon for single-action fire.

the HK P7 with its rivals

SIG-Sauer P226

Also at the top of the range in 9-mm pistols, the SIG-Sauer P226 is utterly reliable, very tough and superbly accurate. Unfortunately this does not come cheap, and it was largely on cost grounds that the P226 failed to win the last US Army pistol selection competition. Most of the parts are from the existing P220 and P225 weapons, which are classy weapons in themselves.

Specification:
Cartridge: 9-mm Parabellum
Weight: 840 g (empty)
Length: 19.6 cm
Barrel length: 11.2 cm
Magazine: 15 rounds

Assessment
Reliability ★★★★
Accuracy ★★★★
Age ★★
Worldwide users ★

The SIG-Sauer range of superb quality pistols are generally more accurate but have high price tags.

Walther P5

One of Heckler and Koch's main rivals for German police orders, the Walther P5 meets the exacting safety standards required by the police but can still fire double action without any fiddling about with safety levers. A locked-breech, recoil-operated pistol, it will not fire if dropped or even if the hammer is tripped when hand-cocking the weapon.

Specification:
Cartridge: 9 mm Parabellum
Weight: 795 g (empty)
Length: 18 cm
Barrel length: 9 cm
Magazine: 8 rounds

Assessment
Reliability ★★★★
Accuracy ★★★
Age ★★★
Worldwide users ★★

The Walther P5 is another pistol designed with police use in mind. hence the extra safety devices.

Beretta 92F

Competition in the 9 mm pistol world is fiercer now than ever and the Beretta family produces several top contenders now facing the Heckler and Koch range. The 92 series of 9 mm autos offers something for everyone and as a straight military pistol, the 92F is difficult to surpass. With a comfortable two handed grip and clear sight picture, the 92F shoots well and may be preferred by those who do not like the H&K P7's squeeze cocking system.

Specification:
Cartridge: 9-mm Parabellum
Weight: 950 g (empty)
Length: 21.7 cm
Barrel length: 12.5 cm
Magazine: 15 rounds

Assessment
Reliability ★★★★
Accuracy ★★★★
Age ★★
Worldwide users ★★★

Accurate and with a large magazine capacity, the Beretta 92F is a sound choice for 9mm combat pistol.

Stingray - Lightweight Champion

The Commando Stingray Light Tank has been developed as a private venture by the Cadillac Gage company in recognition of the growing importance of the light tank to military thinking all over the world. Stingray has been designed to meet some exacting criteria for a light tank. It has plenty of firepower – its 105-mm gun will accept a range of NATO ammunition – and a large operational range. It's light and can be transported easily, and has a low profile for increased survivability. And it's built from proven components.

Stingray's initial development began in January 1983. Design work began in September that year and prototype construction in the following February. The completed prototype appeared at the Association of the United States Army (AUSA) meeting in Washington in October 1984. Since then, it has successfully completed a series of rigorous durability trials.

Light and dark

The hull of the Stingray is all-welded Cadloy steel armour, which

Left: Light enough to be carried by a Lockheed C-130 Hercules, Stingray's armour can be penetrated by 20-mm cannon, so despite its aggressive appearance Stingray must hit first to survive.

will withstand a 14.5-mm armour-piercing round over the frontal arc, and a 7.62-mm round elsewhere. Stingray will be able to withstand a frontal attack from the heaviest Soviet machine gun, but not from the new generation of cannon mounted on the BMP-2, Bradley and Warrior.

The layout is conventional, with the driver's compartment at the front, fighting compartment in the centre and engine and transmission at the rear. Seated in a cupola in the centre front of the hull, the driver has a single-piece hatch cover hinged at the rear. Three forward-looking peri-

Above: Firing with the turret fully traversed imposes the greatest strain on the turret ring, but Stingray has triumphed in an exhaustive series of tests.

side of the compartment. Although a spall blanket can be fitted to the rear and sides of the driver when in action this would offer little protection should the ammunition take a direct hit from an armour-piercing round.

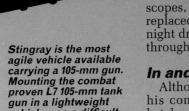

Stingray is the most agile vehicle available carrying a 105-mm gun. Mounting the combat proven L7 105-mm tank gun in a lightweight vehicle was a difficult engineering task, but Cadillac-Gage and Royal Ordnance have developed a soft recoil system which can cope with the formidable shock of firing 105-mm APFSDS rounds.

scopes, the centre one of which can be replaced by a passive periscope for night driving, give excellent visibility through 120 degrees.

In and out

Although the driver can easily enter his compartment through his own hatch when the turret is traversed to the left or right, he can also get in through the main turret – a privilege denied drivers of the majority of main battle tanks, who are effectively trapped when the gun barrel is pointing forward!

Rather uncomfortably for the driver, 14 rounds of 105-mm ready-use ammunition are stored on each

Drive on . . .

Unusually for so large a vehicle, the Stingray is controlled by a steering wheel rather than the conventional sticks. Suspension is of the torsion bar type and similar to that employed in the tried and tested M109 155-mm self-propelled howitzer. The six dual rubber-tyred road wheels are complemented by a drive sprocket at the rear, idler at the front and three tank return rollers "borrowed" from the M41 Walker Bulldog.

Although the basic Stingray weighs only 1,588 kg (3,495 lbs), the suspension has been designed to accept a weight of 1,814 kg (3,990 lb) to allow for modifications (including appliqué armour) without expensive alterations.

Right: Stingray's lightweight chassis and 535-hp V-8 diesel engine gives a superb cross-country performance. It can accelerate to 22 mph in six seconds and has a top speed of 43 mph. It is an attractive option to the armies of emergent nations which need a tank capable of knocking out any likely opponent but better suited to rough terrain.

Inside the Stingray

Stingray is designed to be the most agile tracked vehicle carrying the firepower of a Main Battle Tank. This is made possible by the unique soft recoil 105-mm gun and turret developed jointly by Royal Ordnance in the UK and Cadillac Gage in the USA.

Meteorological sensor

Commander's sight
This is an NV-52 day/night sight. He also has seven periscopes for all-round observation.

Gunner's sight
The gunner uses a Optic-Electronic Corporation M36E1 day/night sight which can be replaced by a sight incorporating a laser rangefinder.

Cadillac Gage three-man turret
The turret has been developed to fit on a variety of vehicles, including Cadillac Gage V600, M41 and M551 light tanks or even old MBTs like M47s, M48s or T-54.

.50-cal Browning machine-gun

Loader
Stingray has eight round of ready 105-mm ammunition stowed in front of the loader. Another 24 rounds are carried in the front of the hull. All ammunition is below the turret ring.

Commander

Gunner

Cadloy armour
The hull is of all-welded Cadloy steel armour, which provides excellent ballistic protection for its weight. The Stingray is designed to be carried in a C-130 Hercules, so the weight must be kept down. Stingray's armour could be increased if a customer did not require the tank to be so easily air-portable.

Powerpack

The Stingray is powered by the eight-cylinder General Motors Detroit Diesel Model 8V-92 TA engine, developing 535 bhp at 2,300 rpm, with an Allison Division XTG-411-2Am automatic transmission (also found in the M107, M109 and M110 self-propelled guns. Although the engine is mounted crossways to make maximum use of the available space, daily maintenance is made comparatively simple by a series of panels above and at the rear of the engine. These open outwards, to provide excellent access.

The 757-litre integral fuel tank, which sits between the crew and engine compartments, allows a maximum range of 483 km at a cruising speed of 40 km/h. The engine is powerful enough to push the Stingray to a maximum speed of 69 km/h on the flat, and up gradients of 60 per cent. The tank accelerates from 0 to 32 km/h in only 6 seconds.

Three-vane axial fans, working in conjunction with large radiators and oil coolers, let the vehicle operate in temperatures of up to 120°F, while its specially designed batteries give cold-starting down to −25°F. An extra-heavy-duty air cleaner scavenges heavier dirt into the engine exhaust, so that the Stingray can not only operate in extremes of temperature but also in the worst of sand, dust and snow storms.

Firepower

The combat-proven Royal Ordnance 105-mm L7A3 tank gun – first used on the British Centurion and now operational throughout the world – provides the main armament. With a muzzle brake and with a new fume extractor and recoil system to enable it to operate in so light a vehicle, the Low Recoil Force (LRF) gun retains the accuracy and rate of fire of the original and will fire any NATO 105-mm ammunition. Resupply will not be a problem anywhere in the world.

Previous attempts at fitting a tank-killing gun on a light chassis have met with ignominious failure. The M551 Sheridan, seen here in Vietnam, carried a 152-mm gun/missile launcher which never worked properly and had to be withdrawn.

Flat plates
By protecting the turret with flat slabs of armour, the Stingray's designers have made it relatively easy to up-armour the vehicle with the addition of ceramic plates or reactive armour.

Frontal protection
Stingray's frontal armour will keep out small-arms fire and heavy machine-guns up to and including the Soviet 14.5-mm KPVT. The remainder of the vehicle is only armoured against 7.62-mm armour-piercing rounds.

L7 105-mm gun
Firing British and US APFSDS rounds, the L7 is an orthodox rifled gun with a horizontal sliding breech. This enables Stingray to take on a Main Battle Tank.

Muzzle brake

Driver
The driver normally enters his position via the turret; he can only clamber in through the top if the turret is traversed fully right or left or the gun is in its travel lock. With 14 rounds of 105-mm ammunition each side of him, the driver can hang a spall blanket around his position.

Double-pin tracks with detachable pads

Third World purchasers of old Soviet tanks have found the after sales service to be very bad. Stingray is at least a modern vehicle, more reliable and backed by a proven logistic programme from Cadillac Gage.

of Soviet tanks — and, indeed, any vehicle with a chassis weight over 13 tonnes.

The gunner, who is seated to the right below and forward of the commander, has a roof-mounted Optic-Electronic Corporation M36E1 day/night sight. This may be replaced by a SIRE day/night sight, incorporating a laser rangefinder, or a thermal sight. The commander himself has an NV-52 day/night sight with seven periscopes for all-round vision.

The turret can be controlled electro-hydraulically by either the com-

Thirty-six rounds of ammunition are carried in the well of the chassis, with eight for immediate use in the turret, stowed vertically to the left of the breech with the rest under the spent case ejection bag. Three of the ready-to-use rounds are stored in individual racks, which can be pivoted forward to allow virtually instantaneous reaction against an enemy. Unlike the more modern 120-mm tank ammunition, the rounds do not self-combust. Instead, used shells are collected in the case ejection bag and disposed of through the ammunition resupply hatch in the left side of the turret.

On top
The three-man turret itself is also built of all-welded Cadloy steel armour, and has been designed to fit the Cadillac Gage V-300, the Bulldog, the United States M 551, the majority

Low vehicle weight also allows Stingray to traverse soft sand or boggy ground with much greater success than any other tank armed with a 105-mm gun. The 38-cm wide track exerts a ground pressure of only .71 kg/cm.

A 7.62-mm M240 machine gun is mounted co-axially to the left of the main armament. It is provided with 400 rounds of ready-use ammunition supported by a further 2,000 rounds stowed in 200-round boxes. A 7.62-mm or 12.5-mm anti-aircraft machine-gun, mounted above the commander's cupola, and four electronically operated smoke dischargers, mounted either side of the turret, complete the firepower.

The British Marconi Command and Control Systems Digital Fire Control System (DFCS) has been fitted to the prototype, as has a standard M13A1 ventilated face mask NBC protection system.

Day/night sights, a laser rangefinder and the Marconi DFCS digital fire control system and full stabilisation give Stingray a good first-round hit probability.

mander or gunner. It also has a manual back-up, and can traverse through 360 degrees. The gun itself can be traversed from −7.5 to +18 degrees.

Battlefield Evaluation: comparing

Stingray

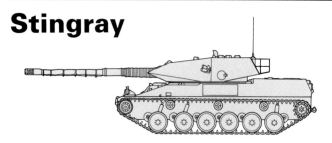

Thailand recently became the first country to buy Stingray. The Thai army had found its M48 and Type 69 tanks were too heavy for the waterlogged terrain and that Stingray, weighing under 20 tonnes but carrying a 105-mm gun, was a better bet. It is also easier to maintain and simpler to operate than an ageing MBT.

Specification:
Crew: 4
Combat weight: 19.3 tonnes
Road speed: 67 km/h
Power to weight ratio: 27.75 hp/tonne
Length: 6.2 m
Height: 2.55 m
Armament: 1×105-mm gun; 1×7.62-mm machine-gun; 1×.50-cal machine-gun

Assessment
Firepower ★★★★
Protection ★★
Age ★
Worldwide users ★

Stingray offers 105-mm firepower in a lightweight, air-portable modern vehicle.

Steyr SK 105 Kurassier

The Austrian army uses the Kurassier as a tank destroyer rather than as a light tank proper. The oscillating turret, protected by 40mm of armour, is similar to that on the French AMX-13 and is similarly fed by two revolver-type magazines. It mounts a 105-mm gun firing spin-stabilised HEAT or a more effective APFSDS round developed by GIAT in France.

Specification:
Crew: 3
Combat weight: 17.5 tonnes
Road speed: 65 km/h
Power to weight ratio: 18.2 hp/tonne
Length: 5.58 m
Height: 2.52 m
Armament: 1×105-mm gun; 1×7.62-mm machine-gun

Assessment
Firepower ★★★
Protection ★★
Age ★★★★
Worldwide users ★

The Kurassier's 105-mm spin-stabilised HEAT rounds are not as effective as APFSDS from an L7.

AMX-13

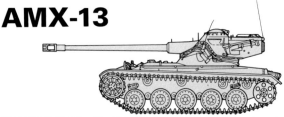

Now offered for sale with night driving kit, laser rangefinder and passive night firing equipment, the AMX-13 soldiers on despite its lack of deep wading capability or NBC system. It shares with the Kurassier the ability to bang out 105-mm rounds every five seconds or so, until its revolver magazines are empty. This sort of hail of fire is useful given the usual two-round tank engagement but, without better ammunition, 105-mm guns will soon be unable to penetrate the new generation of Soviet MBTs.

Specification:
Crew: 3
Combat weight: 15 tonnes
Road speed: 60 hp/tonne
Power to weight ratio: 16.6 hp/tonne
Length: 4.88 m
Height: 2.3 m
Armament: 1×75-, 90- or 105-mm gun; 1×7.5- or 7.62-mm machine-gun

Assessment
Firepower ★★★
Protection ★★
Age ★★★★★
Worldwide users ★★★★

Defying all probability, modernised versions of the AMX-13 are still on offer.

The family

Whereas a land navigation system, an engine smoke generator and fire-warning and suppression systems can be fitted as extras, as yet no large-scale variants of the Stingray exist. However, it is showing all the signs of being a great export success. It is more than likely, therefore, that numerous variants will be introduced within the next few years.

Stingray is designed to kill MBTs, but its greatest enemies will be APCs or armoured cars with automatic cannon, which can obtain hits quickly thanks to their rate of fire. Some potential customers have already asked for extra armour.

the Stingray with its rivals

M41 Walker Bulldog

Built in the early 1950s, the M41 followed the lines of the M24 Chaffee used in World War II. The M41 was supplied in large numbers to South Vietnam since their light weight made them more suitable for the terrain than M48s. They became known as 'voting machines' owing to their regular appearance in Saigon during the military coups. The M41 is still used in Latin America and modernised versions are available.

Specification:
Crew: 4
Combat weight: 23.49 kg
Road speed: 72 km/h
Power to weight ratio: 21.26 hp/tonne
Length: 5.8 m
Height: 2.7 m
Armament: 1×76-mm gun; 1×7.62-mm machine-gun; 1×.50-cal machine-gun

Assessment
Firepower ★★
Protection ★★★
Age ★★★★★
Worldwide users ★★

The M41's greatest weakness today is its gun, but it can be fitted with the same turret as Stingray.

FMC Close Combat Vehicle Light

The CCV L was developed by Ford in anticipation of a US Army funded project for a new light tank. Designed to fit in a C-130 Hercules, the CCV L can bolt on extra protection if required. This could include reactive armour, which would at least give a sporting chance against RPG-7-type fire. The gun is a modified M68A1 with West German low recoil system and digital fire control.

Specification:
Crew: 3
Combat weight: 19.4 tonnes
Road speed: 70 km/h
Power to weight ratio: 26 hp/tonne
Length: 6.1 m
Height: 2.69 m
Armament: 1×105-mm gun; 1×7.62-mm machine-gun

Assessment
Firepower ★★★
Protection ★★
Age ★
Worldwide users ★

The FMC CCV L is a direct commercial rival to Stingray developed for the US Army.

AAI RDF light tank

The Rapid Deployment Force light tank is another private venture developed to prototype stage originally for a US Army programme. Rather than fiddle about with low recoil systems for existing 105-mm guns, the AAI vehicle carries an automatic 75-mm cannon able to fire APFSDS shells with long rod, high density penetrators at a rate of 70 shells per minute.

Specification:
Crew: 3
Combat weight: 13.4 tonnes
Road speed: 64 km/h
Power to weight ratio: 26 hp/tonne
Length: 5.5 m
Height: 2.28 m
Armament: 1×75-mm ARES cannon; 1×7.62-mm machine-gun

Assessment
Firepower ★★
Protection ★★
Age ★
Worldwide users ★

The AAI, like the latest Soviet armour, lacks a conventional turret and uses an external mounting.

The BMD and the Blue Berets

Soviet Airborne Forces (Voz-dushov Desantiye Voyska, or VDV) have recently been transformed into powerful mechanized units, capable of seizing defended objectives and attacking well-armed forces deep in the enemy rear. Unlike British paratroopers, who drop with minimum arms and equipment and rely on speed and aggression to win the day, Soviet airborne forces have a complete series of specialized vehicles that match all but the strongest allied forces in firepower and manoeuvrability.

Boyevaya Mashina Desantnaya — the BMD

The BMD airborne amphibious infantry combat vehicle entered service in 1973 and at a stroke turned the VDV from light to mechanized infantry. Because of outward similarities, it is often mistaken for the BMP, but it has a totally new hull design and suspension, is far lighter, and is considerably more cramped inside.

The BMD can be carried in the hull of either the Il-76 'Candid' or An-12 'Cock' which, between them, account for the majority of Soviet military air transport. With its pneumatic suspension system folded up the BMD can be dropped from the air.

The vehicle is pulled from the rear of the aircraft with the aid of a drogue chute. Then the main canopy deploys, and four probe poles unfold beneath the pallet. As soon as one of the poles makes contact with the ground, a retro-rocket system fires, considerably slowing the final stages of descent. The crew drop immediately after their vehicle and, during night drops, are guided to it by a radio "bleeper". They detach the pallet restraints and are operational in a matter of minutes.

The BMD's main armament is the same 73mm low-pressure smoothbore gun as that mounted on the BMP. Although ineffective against the latest NATO tank armour, the high explosive anti-tank (HEAT) round will penetrate the much thinner skins of Western infantry combat vehicles, but is only accurate to 800 metres. The BMD is itself very lightly protected (there is no more than 25mm of armour in the turret front and 15mm in the hull) – making it easy prey for the 25mm Chain Gun mounted on both the United States' Bradley and the British Warrior.

Power and problems

A rear-mounted Type 5D-20 V-6 liquid cooled diesel engine which develops 240hp powers the BMD. It has a maximum road speed of 80km/h and through water, aided by two water jets mounted in the rear, can reach 10km/h. The driver is seated centrally, immediately in front of the small one-man turret. Either the squad commander or gunner, seated to the left and right of the driver, can fire the section RPK machine-gun.

The main armament is unstabilized and, despite the help of a co-axial 7.62-mm PKT machine-gun, is very inaccurate when fired on the move. The automatic loader and 40 rounds of ready-to-use ammunition take up much of the remaining space inside, leaving room for only three passengers. Two AT-3 'Sagger' missiles are carried inside and can be fired from a rail above the gun barrel.

Despite its excellent reputation, the BMD does have a number of drawbacks. The 'Sagger' demands and unbroken line of sight between firer and target, and cannot be reloaded by the crew unless they break the vehicle's NBC seal.

The fuel tanks are poorly constructed and have a marked tendency to break away from their mountings, while the additional tanks in the rear are vulnerable to incendiary fire.

A BMD-2 M1979/3 command vehicle in Afghanistan with its antenna raised. The BMD-2 M1979 series is distinguishable by the sixth road wheel and the absence of a turret. Another version carries twin AGS-17 automatic 30-mm grenade launchers and two bow-mounted 7.62-mm machine-guns.

Finally, the transmission is too fragile to withstand heavy drops – with the result that the shift lever can disengage at critical moments, leaving the vehicle helplessly stuck in gear.

Variations on the BMD

The most important, if least known, of the BMD family is the BMD-2 air assault transporter. First seen during the 1979 invasion of Afghanistan (and thus often called the BMD M1979 in the West), the BMD-2 is 60cm longer than the original, has an extra road wheel and return roller, and a built-up superstructure but no turret.

Two basic variants exist of which

the BMD M1979/1 multi-purpose armoured transporter is the more common. Used for route control in larger drops and as a prime mover whenever support weapons such as the ZU-23 or Vasilek mortar are deployed, the transporter can also carry up to nine fully equipped troops. Each soldier has a firing port, two capable of taking automatic weapons in the bow, two in the front hatches, two per side and one in the rear. The other variant, known as the BMD M1973/3 or BMD-2KSh, is a command vehicle equipped with a folding "clothes line" antenna round the superstructure, a single commander's hatch, and no fire ports.

There have been important changes in armament in a number of the newer BMDs. The 73mm smooth-bore gun has been replaced by a far more accurate 30mm autocannon (also mounted on the BMP-2), while the AT-4 'Spigot' has been mounted in place of the old AT-3 'Sagger'. 'Spigot' (known informally as "Milanski", because of its marked similarity to MILAN) has a range of 2,000 metres and can be taken from the vehicle and used on the

Above: *First observed in public three years ago, the SO-120 fire support vehicle carries an enlarged turret mounting a long-barrelled 120-mm mortar. This is replacing the ageing ASU-85 assault/anti-tank gun. The breech loading mortar is believed to carry a* **HEAT** *round for anti-tank action.*

Below: *Parading in Moscow, 7 November 1980, this* **BMD** *carries an AT-3 'Sagger' anti-tank guided missile on its launcher rail above the 73-mm smoothbore gun. The tiny size of the vehicle compared to the crew is readily apparent; the* **BMD** *is even more cramped than the* **BMP**.

The old **ASU**-57 self-propelled anti-tank gun on its pallet behind an Antonov An-12 'Cub' tactical transport. **ASU**-57s probably made their last combat appearance in the Ogaden desert during 1978 and are no longer in front-line service.

A **BMD**-1 in Afghanistan where Soviet airborne forces spearheaded the initial invasion in 1979 and later formed the cutting edge of the Soviet war effort against the Mujahideen. This **BMD**-1 appears to have lost its 'Sagger' launching rail.

Inside the BMD

The BMD APC is air-dropped as part of a Soviet airborne operation and provides Soviet paratroops with increased mobility and firepower. It is seen here in action in Afghanistan.

ground. However, it can only be fired *from* the vehicle if a crewman opens one of the rear hatches and leans forward. In this position, he is completely unprotected and would break the NBC seal if the NBC system were operating.

Fire support

Until 1985, Soviet airborne troops were forced to rely on the D-30 122mm towed field howitzer for artillery support, and on the ASU-85 for limited anti-tank protection. Whereas the D-30 was powerful enough to engage the majority of rear-echelon enemy artillery, it was too cumbersome to be towed by anything smaller than a BMD-2. The ASU-85, self-propelled, fast and manoeuvrable though it was, was far too small to engage modern MBTs.

The problem was partly resolved in 1985 by the introduction of the 2S9 assault artillery vehicle: a 120mm breech-loading mortar, mounted in a large turret on a BMD-2 chassis.

A small stub charge boosts the projectile out of the barrel, when a rocket motor cuts in to accelerate the round to cruise speed. Although not as accurate as the ground forces' 122mm 2S1 howitzer, the 9-tonne 2S9 is light enough to be air-droppable. Its extremely high elevation lets it take on downhill targets (particularly important in Afghanistan) while in direct fire its HEAT round will penetrate all but the latest generation of tanks and will prove lethal when engaging APCs. Neither the range nor rate of fire are known, but experts believe the mortar may well be fitted with a semi-automatic loading system, with burst-fire potential.

Air defence

A Soviet airborne division relies on 48 SA-9 'Gaskin' Surface-to-Air Missiles. Designed originally for low-level regimental defence, the SA-9 missile is derived from the SA-7 'Grail' but has a larger warhead, more powerful motor and improved controls. Carried in two double mounts on an adapted BRDM-2 vehicle, the missile is launched by its operator once he has acquired the target optically. Without up-to-date radar assistance 'Gaskin' can hope to have only very limited success against modern fast jets. But its usefulness against helicopters, probably the airborne soldier's greatest threat, is considerably greater.

Three SA-7 'Grail' hand-held launchers are issued to the air defence section of each airborne company. Perhaps the most famous system of its kind in the world, the basic missile consists of a tube with a dual-thrust solid motor steered by canard fins. Once the operator has located the target through his open sights, he simply takes the first pressure on the trigger,

15 mm hull armour
The thin frontal armour of the BMD is just enough to keep out small arms fire, but nothing larger.

2A28 73-mm smoothbore gun
Loaded automatically from a 40-round magazine, the 73-mm gun fires fin-stabilised, rocket-propelled HEAT and HE-FRAG rounds at up to eight rounds per minute. Its maximum range is 1300 metres, but it is badly affected by wind.

7.62-mm PKT machine-gun

Guards of the Order of the Red Banner Airborne Division prepare pontoons for a river-crossing exercise. Soviet airborne troops, like those of the Strategic Rocket Forces, all have pre-induction military training. No other branch of the Soviet Armed Forces insists on this requirement, which is a measure of the importance attached to the seven paratroop divisions.

'Sagger' anti-tank missile
In the early 1980s BMDs were usually seen with a 'Sagger' launcher above the 73-mm gun, as on the BMP. More recent pictures of BMDs show that many now carry a dismountable AT-4 'Spigot' missile.

Turret
The low turret is similar to that of the BMP. The armour is not more than 25-mm thick over the frontal arc and two 'Sagger' missiles are stored within, plus, 2,000 rounds for the co-axial 7.62-mm machine guns.

Gunner
The gunner relies on the familiar Soviet stadiametric rangefinder, in which graticules coincide with different ranges assuming a target height of 2.7 metres (average NATO tank height). He keeps the controls for the 'Sagger' missile under his seat, pulling them out when the vehicle stops to fire a missile.

Commander
Sitting on the driver's left, the commander has access to the gyro-compass and radio.

Driver
The driver sits centrally, observing through three periscopes positioned in front of his hatch. IR periscopes are available for night driving.

Troop compartment
This is small, able to accommodate only three men in relative comfort, although more can be included. The only means of access is via a concertina-type hatch in the roof.

Periscope

Bow machine-gunner
Sitting behind and to the right of the driver, the bow machine-gunner operates the twin 7.62-mm PKT machine-guns.

Ground clearance
The independent suspension has a hydraulic mechanism for maintaining track tension and alternating ground clearance between 10 and 45 cm.

Idler

Road wheel

Track return roller

Drive sprocket

AT-3 'Sagger' anti-tank guided missile

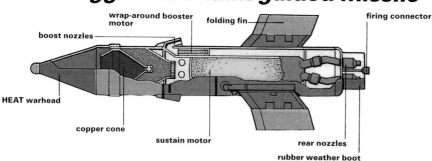

Labels: wrap-around booster motor, folding fin, firing connector, boost nozzles, HEAT warhead, copper cone, sustain motor, rear nozzles, rubber weather boot

AT-3 'Sagger' is the primary anti-tank weapon of the BMD, since the 73-mm gun is inaccurate over 800 m and only able to penetrate lightly armoured targets. With a minimum range of 300 m and a maximum range of 3000 m, 'Sagger' flies at 120 metres per second. It has little launch signature, just a small puff of grey smoke which you are unlikely to see. However, the large rocket flies relatively slowly and leaves a short smoke trail, making it fairly easy to detect.

waits for the red light to turn green – indicating that the seeker has locked on – and applies full pressure to the trigger. The 2.5kg warhead is lethal only against small targets but can nevertheless force a large aircraft to abort its attack.

Infantry support

Among the latest, and finest, pieces of equipment to enter service with the VDV has been the AGS-17, or *Plamya*, which is now issued to the support section of each company. The AGS-17 is an automatic 30mm grenade launcher; with maximum and effective ranges of 1,500 and 800 metres respectively, and its staggering rate of

Battlefield Evaluation: comparing

BMD

Each of the seven Soviet airborne divisions can field 330 of these armoured personnel carriers, which give Soviet paratroopers a substantial advantage over their Western counterparts. Nearly six tons lighter than the BMP from which it is developed, the BMD can be dropped by parachute and is fully amphibious. It has obvious limitations as an APC, principally its lack of room, but in the right place at the right time it could make all the difference.

Specification:
Crew: 2+6
Combat weight: 8.9 tonnes
Road speed: 80 km/h
Power to weight ratio: 35 hp/tonne
Length: 5.4 m
Height: 1.85 m
Armament: 1×73-mm smoothbore gun; 1 launcher rail for 'Sagger' or 'Spigot' anti-tank missiles; 1×7.62-mm machine-gun

Assessment
Firepower ★★★★★
Protection ★★
Age ★★★
Worldwide users ★

The BMD provides Soviet paratroops with tremendous mobility and fire support.

ASU-85

Soviet airborne divisions also include a 31-tank battalion of ASU-85 tank destroyers. Based on the PT-76 chassis, the ASU-85 is armed with a World War II vintage 85-mm gun which is not much use against modern tanks. As a result it is being phased out of service. Since the BMDs carry anti-tank missiles there is no need for a replacement air-droppable tank destroyer, and its place is being taken by the SO-122 (2S9) self-propelled mortar.

Specification:
Crew: 4
Combat weight: 14 tonnes
Road speed: 45 km/h
Power to weight ratio: 13.5 hp/tonne
Length: 6 m
Height: 2.1 m
Armament: 1×85-mm gun; 1×7.62-mm machine-gun

Assessment
Firepower ★★
Protection ★★
Age ★★★★★
Worldwide users ★

The ASU-85 is unable to knock out the latest NATO tanks and will probably be replaced soon.

ASU-57

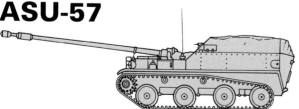

Last appearing in the Ogaden war in 1978, the ASU-57 tank destroyer is no longer in service with the Soviet forces, although it may be retained for training. Like the ASU-85, its armament dates back to World War II and is unable to penetrate the armour of modern tanks. The ASU-57 has the benefit of being truly air-droppable; whereas the ASU-85 is theoretically able to come down by parachute, the Soviets usually prefer to fly it in underneath a Mi-6 'Hook' or Mi-10 'Harke' helicopter.

Specification:
Crew: 3
Combat weight: 3.3 tonnes
Road speed: 45 km/h
Power to weight ratio: 16.4 hp/tonne
Length: 4.9 m
Height: 1.1 m
Armament: 1×57-mm Ch-51 gun

Assessment
Firepower ★
Protection ★
Age ★★★★★
Worldwide users ★

The ASU-57 is air-droppable but no longer of much value once on the DZ. It may be retained as a training vehicle.

fire of 65 missiles per minute, *Plamya* would play a crucial role in suppressing enemy trench defences immediately before and during a final assault.

Each airborne soldier is armed with a 5.45mm AKS-74 assault rifle capable of firing single rounds or automatic bursts and accurate to a range of 500 metres. It is obvious that Soviet airborne units have a firepower second to none. Operating as totally self-contained entities, they can overcome enemy defences, defeat APC mounted and heliborne assaults, and defend themselves from armoured or airborne retaliation.

*Airborne divisions have 48 **SA-9** 'Gaskin' launchers carried on modified **BRDM-2s. SA-9** is an enlarged and improved **SA-7** with a heavier warhead and better discrimination between heat sources. Of limited value against fast jets, it is more effective against helicopters.*

---

the BMD with its rivals

M551 Sheridan

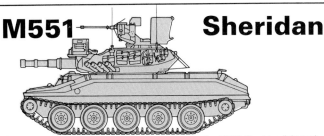

Once the great white hope of US airborne forces, the M551 Sheridan light tank has not been a success. Its 152-mm gun/missile launcher produces too much recoil for the sighting equipment and the chassis to survive. Used in Vietnam, it aroused mixed reaction: some units reported favourably, citing its cross-country capability and powerful armament. Others rejected it as mechanically unreliable and poorly protected. Only 54 M551s remain in service, all with 82nd Airborne.

Specification:
Crew: 4
Combat weight: 15.8 tonnes
Road speed: 70 km/h
Power to weight ratio: 18.95 hp/tonne
Length: 6.29 m
Height: 2.27 m
Armament: 1×152-mm gun/missile launcher; 1×12.7-mm and 1×7.62-mm machine-guns

Assessment
Firepower	★★★★★
Protection	★★
Age	★★★
Worldwide users	★

The Sheridan was an expensive failure, and only a handful still remain in service.

Wiesel

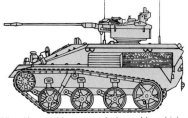

Developed by Porsche, the Wiesel is a multi-purpose air-droppable vehicle produced for the West German airborne forces. It can be slung beneath a Puma helicopter and is easily air-portable; a C-130 can carry three of them. It can carry a variety of armament fits, the West German airborne units will use one version fitted with a 20-mm cannon as a recce vehicle and another, armed with TOW ATGW, as a tank destroyer. Other weapons fits available include HOT ATGW, Stinger SAMs or 25-mm cannon.

Specification:
Crew: 2 (20-mm gun) 3 (TOW)
Combat weight: 2.75 tonnes
Road speed: 80 km/h
Power to weight ratio: 30.72 hp/tonne
Length: 3.26 m
Height: 1.99 m (20-mm gun); 1.87 m (TOW)
Armament: 20-mm cannon or TOW missiles

Assessment
Firepower	★★★★
Protection	★
Age	★
Worldwide users	★

*Wiesel is an exciting new vehicle with a great deal of potential for **NATO** airborne forces.*

Light Armoured Vehicle

The Canadian version of the Swiss MOWAG Piranha is used by the US Marines and is air-portable beneath a CH-53 helicopter as well as amphibious. Of the 149 LAVs in a USMC LAV battalion, 56 are armed with 25-mm Chain Guns and there are assault gun, anti-tank missile, anti-aircraft missile and mortar-carrying versions.

Specification:
Crew: 3+6
Combat weight: 13 tonnes
Road speed: 100 km/h
Power to weight ratio: 23.4 hp/tonne
Length: 6.39 m
Height: 2.69 m
Armament: various

Assessment
Firepower	★★★★
Protection	★★
Age	★★
Worldwide users	★★

*The **US** Marine Corps continues to expand its force of **LAVs**.*

Abandon Ship!

A Royal Navy Sea King plucks survivors from the water after the landing ship HMS Sir Galahad was set alight by an Argentine air strike on 14 June 1982. In some emergencies at sea you may have little influence on events, but on other occasions your knowledge of the emergency drills could make all the difference.

Evacuation must be well timed: here the Sea Cat missile magazine on HMS Antelope explodes, ignited by the fire which followed the detonation of an 1,000-lb bomb during an attempt to defuse it. The explosion came just minutes after the last man left.

The incoming missile, sweeping low over the surface of the sea, gives little audible warning. You're sitting on your bunk below when it strikes with the noise of a giant sledgehammer hitting a monster oil drum. Everything shudders out of focus with the impact. Tiny paint particles splinter from the bulkhead and the deck drops in a stomach-churning corkscrew as your feet touch, then rises to send you staggering.

The lights dim beneath sudden thick billows of oily smoke as the siren on the funnel far above begins to wail . . .

The sea is the oldest and toughest enemy of mankind. At best it is unforgiving, at worst it is blindly malicious. As over 70 per cent of the earth's surface is covered in deep salt water, military personnel have to cross it constantly, either by surface vessel or aircraft, and it is only sensible to be prepared to combat this enemy as you would any other.

Assume the worst

First of all – without giving away to alarm and despondency – when you board an aircraft or ship, assume the worst. Each craft will display an Emergency Station Card (ESC), showing the stations allocated to the crew in the event of fire and general emergency, the places where firefighting equipment and liferafts are kept, and the duties of each crew member once it has become necessary to take up these stations.

Even though you may embark as a passenger, it will do you no harm and take you only a short time to familiarise yourself with the ESC details. In an emergency, the crew may be injured or killed, and you may have to step into the breach at short notice.

Nor should you be embarrassed to ask regular crew members about the emergency equipment: what does it consist of? Is there a full quota of rations and medicines aboard each raft? Most important of all, are there sufficient rafts aboard to go round?

If you are in charge of other personnel it is your duty, to them and yourself, to ask such questions and to get clear answers. Discipline is essential. As soon as an emergency develops, go to your allotted station. If the vessel is doomed, the order to abandon can usually come only from the skipper, and is given either by tannoy or the continuous sounding of alarm bells or the ship's siren.

Fighting fires aboard ship

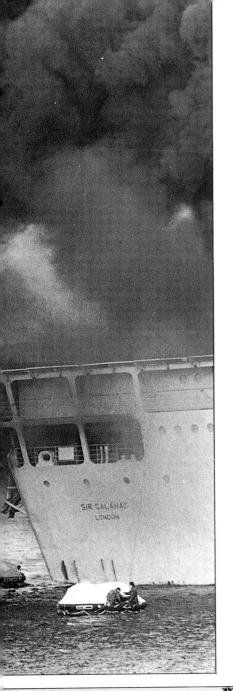

If you have abandoned ship and she remains afloat, it may be possible to re-board her. If you make such an attempt, leave sufficient men behind to handle the life rafts or lifeboats, and have them lie-to well away from the parent vessel.

If fire has broken out, tackling it will be your main priority.

All fires require fuel, oxygen, and heat: remove any one of these and the fire will die. Stopping the air flow is often difficult, but by the correct use of extinguishers the fire may either be smothered or cooled.

Aboard ship four types of extinguisher will usually be found, each with its distinguishing international colour code and content for tackling different types of blaze:

1 A **red canister** contains water, which should ONLY be used for solid, dry fires in timber, rags, paper and clothing.
2 Liquid fires such as oil or fat should be smothered with foam from the **cream-coloured container**.
3 The **black-painted carbon dioxide (CO_2) canister** can also be used for liquid fires and is essential in dealing with fires in electrical equipment.
4 Dry powder, from the **blue container**, can be used safely in almost any emergency.

Try to close down all electrics at source, and where feasible break out the main firefighting equipment – hoses and pumping gear. Remember that heat and smoke rise, so that by crawling at deck level you will find that not only are conditions cooler and breathing easier, but that you will be able to see to direct the extinguisher at the heart of the fire.

Get rid of combustible material and soak the surrounding area with water sprays; watch out for hidden fire in ventilation trunking, false deckheads and panelling in nearby cabins and compartments.

In Royal Navy ships vaporising liquids such as bromo-chloro-difluoro-methane (BCF) and bromo-trifluoro-methane (BTM) are often used in extinguishers. While these are very effective, you should remember that fumes from them can be dangerous in a confined space like the cabin of a ship, so hatches, doors and port-holes should be opened before spraying with BCF or BTM is attempted.

Great care should always be taken when opening up, however, even though a fire may have appeared to die in a sealed compartment. Heat and fuel will still be present in the area – either solid or gaseous – and only oxygen or additional heat is required to cause an explosion or flash-over fire which will roar up as intensely as ever. Ventilate slowly, carefully and progressively.

In the case of fire in the engine room or galley, an important first step is to prevent air reaching the fire by closing skylights, deck hatches, doors and ventilation systems servicing the areas. Engine rooms are fitted with a steam-smothering system which can be activated by clearly-marked control valves sited outside the immediate danger area.

Re-entry should ONLY be attempted if proper breathing apparatus is available, and should be made by way of the engine room escape tunnel, which is at a low level. A cautious opening of a skylight will draw air through the tunnel, once the flames are out, and force out toxic smoke and fumes. But again, precautions against flash-fires should be taken, preferably by leading a high-powered hose through the tunnel and keeping it at the ready.

If the fires are quelled and a pump can be rigged to drain off water from the bilges, the men in the lifeboats can be helped back on board. Do not attempt to re-ship the lifeboats, however; lash down the movable gear in them, and moor them to the hull for a quick getaway should a further emergency develop.

HMS Sheffield was struck by an Exocet missile, which did not explode, but half a ton of rocket travelling at over 700 mph tore into the ship and started a fierce fire. With all power gone and the water supply broken, firefighting efforts were severely hampered. As with the Antelope, the final decision to abandon ship was taken as the fire neared the magazine.

If time permits put on as many clothes as possible. Wear sweaters under oilskins, wind proofs or combat jackets, and life jackets on top. Grab as many containers with screw tops as you can find – polythene or plastic bottles are ideal – and fill them three quarters full of fresh water so that they will float. Stuff as much food as you can find into pockets, if necessary bundling up tins with empty containers for flotation in a sheet knotted to form a sack. And don't forget a tin opener!

Any equipment which will help to navigate and manage a life raft should be grabbed; lengths of line, mirror for signalling, paper and pencil, hand bearing compass, knife, torch and batteries, first aid kit, extra flares, fishing tackle and a bucket will be invaluable. Finally, try and salvage important

Survival

documents including orders, maps and the ship's papers. Life rafts and lifeboats are sometimes fitted with emergency portable radio transmitters, but if there are any spare, take them with you.

If the ship is not listing too badly it should be possible to launch the lifeboats, but this procedure should be left to experienced crew members where available: lifeboat tackle is easy to jam and notoriously difficult to free. Don't try to enter a lifeboat before it is launched; either jump over the side if the water is clear or abseil down the side of the ship.

Find the life rafts

Life rafts are usually stowed either in fibreglass containers fitted into cradles on deck or in canvas valises which are to be found in either cutaway recesses in funnel or deckhouse casing, or in collapsible wooden boxes fitted to the deck. Both types float in their packing, so even if the lifeboats are successfully launched throw the life rafts overboard too, along with the wooden boxes, which will probably prove useful.

Where the ship has developed a heavy list and you have to climb down the side of the hull on the opposite side, don't try and slide down on your backside. Barnacles, which quickly attach themselves to even the newest of ships below the waterline, lacerate clothing and flesh with equal ease.

Fire is the most terrifying of hazards at sea. If your clothing is burning try to unbutton or unzip it and pull it off: don't tear blindly at it. Roll around on deck to try and smother the blaze.

USS Stark *lists heavily to port after being struck by an Iranian Exocet missile. Like the* Sheffield *her crew was not at full alert when attacked, but the larger vessel survived the explosion.*

Jumping into the sea

If you have to jump from the ship, keep your body vertical. Keep your legs straight, crossed and locked at the ankles, and keep your head erect so that your spinal column is in a straight line. Position your arms as shown, pinching your nose if you like. If you merely keep your legs side by side they may be forced apart on contact with the water and debris can be forced up between them.

If a mate is on fire, smother him with blankets or thick clothing and, if possible, douse the flames with a foam or powder extinguisher. If clothing made of rubber or synthetics is welded to bare flesh by the heat, do not try to remove it. Later in the life raft you may be able to give some relief using first aid.

Complete immersion in sea water will douse petrol or oil burning on clothing, but don't throw a blazing mate over the side, or jump yourself, unless you are absolutely certain that fuel has not leaked from the hull, otherwise you will be applying a human torch to a potential inferno. Try to swim away from the vessel -against- prevailing winds and currents – which will carry any later spillage of oil away from you – and away from suction as the ship goes down.

When a ship sinks, its bulk disappearing beneath the surface will cause a momentary whirlpool which

The burning deck

Fire on board a ship can be indescribably horrific. The only way you can help yourself is to make sure you know the drills beforehand. Even if you are only going to be on board for a short journey, don't leave it all to the crew: take safety instructions seriously.

Clothing
While you don't want to be inside a ship when she sinks or the magazine goes off, spare a thought for the sea conditions before you leap. Diving into the Arctic Ocean in a T-shirt is not a good plan. On the other hand, heavy woollens will weigh you down, so make sure you get a lifejacket on.

Trapped
If the worst happens and you find yourself trapped in a compartment, remember that you can't open a hatch against water pressure. You may have to flood a compartment in order to escape.

Lifeboat drill
Familiarise yourself with the emergency equipment and drills. Don't regard a lifeboat briefing as just an excuse for a breath of fresh air on deck. Ask questions if you don't understand something. Make certain you can don and inflate a lifejacket without problems.

Getting help
You could find yourself entombed in a ship which is floating upside down. When trying to attract attention from rescuers, tapping works better than shouting, which simply uses up more air.

will tend to draw floating objects into its vortex – the bigger the vessel the greater the pull – but, as a general rule, if you can put a distance between you and the sinking ship equal to the height of the vessel from waterline to top superstructure, you should be safe. In other words if the distance from waterline to funnel top is 10 metres, you will have to swim 10 metres to be clear.

However, sea conditions, currents and other factors may alter matters. For instance, when the battleships *Repulse* and *Prince of Wales* were sunk in the Pacific during World War II, deck officers trapped on the bridge reported waiting until the bridge was awash and then stepping off into the water in perfect safety. Other survivors were sucked down with the ships, only to be blown back to the surface by giant bubbles of air escaping from the interior.

*Perversely, the fire aboard **Sheffield** did not lead to a catastrophic explosion and it burned itself out. However, the ship was so badly damaged that she sank under tow on 10 May.*

Learn the way
Knowing your way through the labyrinth of passages and compartments inside a warship or transport is not easy for a non-crew member. If you are being shipped overseas, check out the escape routes from your quarters and learn your way about. Remember, you may have to get out quickly – and possibly in the dark.

Jumping overboard
If at all possible, climb rather than jump into the water. Nets, ladders or ropes offer a safer (but obviously slower) method of escape. If you have to jump, use the position shown and watch out for debris below.

Action in the water
Once in the water, swim away from the ship until you surface. If you bob up where you jumped in, you may get jumped on by another survivor leaping from the deck.

Clinging to the Wreckage

At last it becomes clear that your stricken ship is about to go down. It settles deeper in the water, creaking, and it's time for everyone to get clear. Most of the men are in life rafts sheltering in the lee of the hull, and the rushing of water is their signal to move as far away as possible so that they don't get sucked down with it.

But some of you have been going back on board to collect food and supplies and to man the radio as long as possible, and you have to take to the water in a hurry. In its death throes, the ship rears up for the last time, pointing skywards, and sinks beneath the waves with a hollow roaring sound. From now on your survival depends on three factors: your ability to use the survival equipment available; your ability to adapt your special skills in order to cope with hazards; and, perhaps most important of all, your will to live.

Your first course will be to get clear of fuel-covered water, in case it ignites, and to search for other survivors; at sea as on land there is usually safety in numbers and you should gather together as soon as possible. Remember – co-operation is a key to survival. If there's no room on the life rafts that are near you, grab the largest piece of floating debris you can find, and make a conscious effort to relax. If you can relax and avoid panicky thrashing around, you will, if you are reasonably fit, stand very little danger of drowning in the ocean, for the body's natural buoyancy will help you float. But you will need to keep your face above water by some form of paddling movement – don't exhaust yourself by striking out in an energetic crawl stroke.

If you are waiting for a raft to approach you, your best plan is to roll onto your back and simply float with your arms by your sides and your

hands making finning movements, a position which will automatically lift your face clear. You can also float quite easily by lying face downwards with your legs dangling beneath you; pushing down on the surface with your outstretched hands will lift you sufficiently to take regular breaths.

'Dog paddling' is the easiest stroke to use while swimming in heavy clothing or in a life jacket. The breast stroke should be used for swimming under water – to avoid surface oil or debris for instance – or in rough seas, and if you have to travel any distance you can alternate the breast stroke with a side or back stroke so that some of your muscles are resting all the time.

Action in the water

If you get cramp, you must float while attempting to stretch and massage the cramp away. If you are in an area of burning surface oil or fuel, get

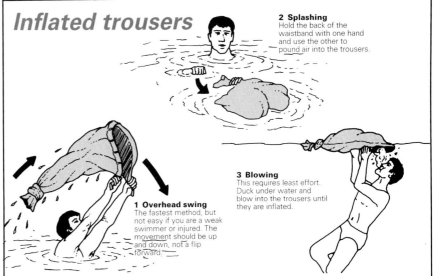

HMS Coventry turns turtle after an Argentine airstrike on 25 May 1982. British media reports that tail-fused Argentine bombs had repeatedly failed to explode had got through to the Argentine air force, who switched to direct-action nose fuses. All three bombs which struck Coventry exploded. The attack was carried out with ordinary 400-kg bombs in clear weather in the face of Sea Harriers and Sea Dart and Sea Wolf missiles.

Inflated trousers

2 Splashing
Hold the back of the waistband with one hand and use the other to pound air into the trousers.

1 Overhead swing
The fastest method, but not easy if you are a weak swimmer or injured. The movement should be up and down, not a flip forward.

3 Blowing
This requires least effort. Duck under water and blow into the trousers until they are inflated.

Even if you are a good swimmer you will eventually become tired, and the effort in keeping afloat can easily lead to panic and drowning. The key to avoiding panic in the water is to create a flotation device that you can hold on to. Floating wreckage is an obvious choice, but if all else fails your trousers can be inflated with air using the methods shown here. Make sure neither leg is inside out, and if you have anything potentially useful in your pockets, secure it elsewhere before taking off your trousers.

rid of your shoes and buoyant life jacket – though you should hang on to an uninflated CO_2 life jacket – and swim as far as possible underwater before surfacing; when you have to surface, sweep your hands as you do so to disperse the flames, and try to face downwind before you inhale.

Once in the raft, the first task is to make it as seaworthy and comfortable as possible, and then tend to the needs of the injured unless anyone obviously needs instant attention - in the case of arterial bleeding, for example.

Among the floating debris from your sunken ship there will probably be a good deal of material that might be of help: containers, clothing and tarpaulin, for instance. These can be either taken on board or, if bulky, lashed to the hand ropes on the raft's hull: make sure that they have no sharp corners to puncture the rubber.

Check the raft for buoyancy – the main buoyancy chambers should be firmly rounded but not drum-tight – and search for leaks, usually along seams or inflation points, and points of possible chafing. Dangerous wear can be made by tow ropes over the side, so wrap any such ropes, including fishing lines, in rag to prevent damage. Make buoyancy checks regularly, and remember that in hot weather air expands, so release some air on hot days; you can always re-inflate when the weather cools.

One of your vital pieces of equipment will be a sea anchor, which should come with the raft. In an emergency you can rig up a sea anchor from

The standard survival priorities – first aid, water supply, shelter and food – all take second place to one thing at sea: flotation. An improvised flotation device is the sea survival equivalent to a warm sleeping bag in the Arctic.

a raft case, bailing bucket, or a heavy rolled-up cloth; the purpose of the sea anchor is to keep the raft headed into wind and waves, thus easing rolling and the possibility of 'broaching to' – turning over sideways in the trough of a wave – and also to slow the raft's drift, if you have decided to stay as near as possible to the ditching site.

Survival

Going down

The sudden transition from warm, safe ship to the cold uncertainty of the sea can easily make you panic, but only by staying calm and rational can you hope to survive.

If there are other rafts in the area, join up and lash them together, using ropes long enough to keep the craft about 10 metres apart so that you do not run the risk of fouling each other. The look-out on each one should be ready to haul his raft close up to his nearest neighbour should an aircraft be seen or heard, so that the aircrew can spot the cluster of rafts more easily.

When tossing a line between craft you should first make a heaving line knot at the end, which is heavy enough to carry the line the maximum distance – about 20 metres – that a man can throw under the circumstances. Rocket-fired lines and metal weights should never be used between rubber rafts because of the damage they may cause to both craft and crew.

Even in calm weather, it is advisable to rig the spray- and wind-shield around the sides of the raft so as to keep the vessel as dry as possible, and in larger rafts a canopy should be kept permanently erected. Make sure that the ballast is properly distributed to balance the boat; heavy men and those who are injured should lie in the centre of the raft – you may have to deflate the cross seats for this purpose, with the rest of the crew and equipment ranged around the hull – and of course in any small boat no sudden or unannounced moves should be made.

Life raft
Do not inflate the life raft until you intend to use it. Launch it from the lee side of the ship: this will protect you from the weather and leaves you well placed to retrieve other survivors of potentially handy floating debris.

Life raft priorities
Once in the water, move away from the sinking ship, deploy a sea anchor and check the buoyancy of your life raft.

Flotation
This remains your first concern: always keep an eye on the buoyancy of the craft. Check that no lines are chaffing the surface of an inflatable, and make sure that leaks are located and plugged.

Collect swimming survivors
Survivors in the water should come aboard from the upwind side. Those already in the craft should help pull people on board.

Treading water

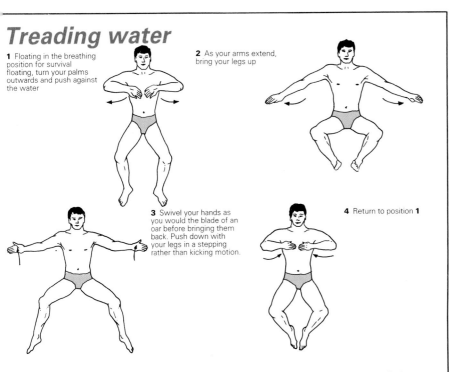

1 Floating in the breathing position for survival floating, turn your palms outwards and push against the water

2 As your arms extend, bring your legs up

3 Swivel your hands as you would the blade of an oar before bringing them back. Push down with your legs in a stepping rather than kicking motion.

4 Return to position **1**

The key to surviving in the water is to relax. You will naturally try to keep your head well clear of the water, but the strain caused by trying to maintain such a stiff vertical position quickly leads to exhaustion. That is a sure route to drowning. Survival floating is the best way to save your energy, but in cold water (72 degrees Fahrenheit or less) immersing the head rapidly cools the body and hypothermia will soon result. Tread water by assuming the breathing position used in survival floating.

Survival floating

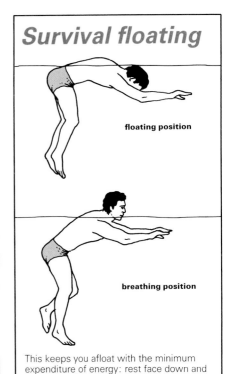

floating position

breathing position

This keeps you afloat with the minimum expenditure of energy: rest face down and come up to breathe in a regular rhythm, breathing out through mouth and nose then in *through the mouth only*. Move your arms in a broad sculling motion; do not press downwards. Draw your legs into a sitting position and 'step' rather than kick down.

Establish a lookout
Arrange a rota of watches as soon as possible. The lookout on duty should be tied to the raft and given extra clothing if the weather is cold. Keep the duration of watches fairly short, say 1½-2 hours, so that the lookout stays alert.

Sea life
Don't trail hands or feet over the side, and use an oar, paddle or anything else handy to ward off inquisitive or even predatory marine life. The movie *Jaws* is very exaggerated but does have a factual basis. Don't clean any fish you catch over the side, and don't allow wounds to bleed into the water.

Leadership
If no officers or NCOs are in your raft, establish a leader aboard your raft. This is not a trivial question: experience shows that having a proper chain of command is vitally important in sea survival.

Swimming
Swim as little as possible: the longer you are in the water, the colder you will become. If possible, enter the water slowly; sudden immersion in chilly water is a horrible shock.

Survival on a Raft

You and your mates have been in the open sea, huddled in your life raft, for 48 hours now. You're snug enough for the moment. The sea anchors are holding you fairly steady, the canopy is up, you have food, water, equipment – and you're alive. Stay put and the odds are that you will be rescued, like the majority of survivors at sea, within seven days. You can't go very far on a raft in a week.

But boredom, damp and perhaps seasickness are beginning to sap morale and, in any case, are you sure that your rescuers will be friendly? When the sinking of your ship set off its buoyed Emergency Position Indicating Radio Beacon (EPIRB) the automatic signals may well have been monitored by the enemy, who could be homing in to either pick you up or pick you off.

If you know that you are within 250 miles of an enemy base, and unless you are sure that friendly forces – ships, aircraft, or land-based – are nearer than that, the radio is best left silent for the moment. If you think that you can make a landfall, start planning to move.

Travel at night

Generally speaking, it will be best to travel only at night, and to lie low – literally – during daylight hours. In military-issue life rafts, your canopy will have two differently-coloured sides; one orange, to attract attention, and the other camouflage green or blue. Make sure the camouflage side is uppermost during the day in hostile waters.

Unless you are in particularly choppy seas, deflate the raft sufficiently for it to lie low on the water –

the lower profile will reduce windage against the sides, as well as prominence – and lie flat in the raft, keeping your sea anchor out. While the rest of the crew tries to rest, the two lookouts – one at each end of the canopy, and each relieved at least once every two hours – should keep their eyes open for signs of land, shifts in the weather conditions, passing ships or aircraft, flocks of birds, schools of fish, tell-tale flotsam from your own or other stricken vessels and other survivors, as well as sharks.

Prepare to move

If ships or aircraft are sited, lookouts should make certain that they are friendly, or at least neutral, before trying to attract their attention.

As dusk begins to fall you can begin making careful preparations for your move. What you are going to try to do

Fastnet disaster

In August 1979 the Fastnet yacht race was overtaken by tragedy as horrific gales struck the racing vessels, sinking over 20 of them. Experienced yachtsmen who had sailed the world over described this storm in the Irish Sea as the worst they had ever seen, with 50-ft waves smashing masts like matchsticks and yachts rolling over in the seething water.

Surviving the initial shipwreck is one problem, but surviving a long period in a life raft can actually be more difficult. The many dangers of the sea may not be the worst threat: the problem is as much psychological as physical. Sighting a distant ship or aircraft immediately builds hope of rescue, so if they turn away without seeing you the despair of hopes raised and then dashed can induce a fatal acceptance of death. Whatever you do, don't give up.

is shift your raft, or flotilla of rafts, in a predetermined direction – if possible to a friendly shore.

With luck, of course, you may have a skilled navigator and/or seaman with you, but in any case you should have a rough idea of where the ship went down, and in the intervening time you will have taken note of the general currents, tides and direction of swells and the times of sunrise and sunset.

Wind and currents

Remember that your raft will move, regardless of what you do; the course it will take depends largely on the wind and the ocean currents, but you can influence matters by intelligent use of oars or paddles, tiller, sea anchor and sails.

If the ocean currents are moving in the direction you want to go but winds

Righting your raft

In rough weather it is doubly important to distribute weight (including passengers) evenly around the raft. Do not sit on the sides or stand up, and never make sudden movements without warning other crew members. Don't tie a fishline to the raft or to yourself: you may catch something large enough to overturn the raft. If it does turn over, use the righting handles on the bottom. Manoeuvre so that you and the bottom side are downwind, grasp the righting handle, and lift the far side of the raft up and over.

A rescue helicopter pulls a man from the water during the Fastnet race disaster. Plucked from the water as storms continued to lash the Irish coast, this crew member later died in hospital.

1315

Fishing hooks

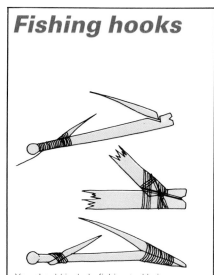

You should include fishing tackle in your survival kit as a matter of course, but if you haven't, you can improvise. You can make up to 50 ft of fishing line from tearing 8-10 strands of fabric from a square yard of dry canvas. Split the bench seats or gunwales to make hooks, and shape the point so that the hardest point of the grain forms the tip and the barb.

boot and lace the boot up tight. Put an extra layer of padding around the boot itself, and jam it under the front cross seat.

Sails can be improvised by using tarpaulin or one or two thicknesses of parachute cloth. In a smaller raft, a combat jacket with an oar thrust through the sleeves as a crossbar makes an ideal sail. Tie a line from each lower corner of the square sail and, as in the case of the guy ropes, get two men to hold the loose ends; with practice they will learn to synchronise their movements so that the sail fills effectively. If any undue strain appears in the sail, one or both should let go and 'spill' the wind.

Haul in the anchor

Before you start to sail, re-inflate the hull of the raft so that it floats high in the water, and haul in the sea anchor. Shortening the sea anchor line, and placing it with its open end inboard inside the raft, is a good idea when sailing, because if the raft capsizes the sea anchor should hit the water at the

The bright orange surface of a raft is obviously designed to attract attention. Some military rafts have double sided coverings so a camouflage blue/green top can be fitted to avoid enemy forces.

are unfavourable, leave the sea anchor out and retain your 'low profile' in the water. The currents will prevail against the wind, but you should not expect to move more than six to eight miles a day. If the wind is 'abaft the beam' – that is, blowing from any point behind the centre line of the boat – you can make progress, relatively fast if the wind is dead astern, but you will need a square sail and a steering oar in the stern. Any multi-place raft except the heavy 20-man vessel will sail in this 'Viking' style.

Making a mast

Some rafts will be fitted with a mast, mast socket and step – the place where the heel of the mast meets the hull – and a proper sail. But if no such equipment is available you can make a mast by lashing two oars together with another as crossbar or yard-arm.

Erect the mast as far forward as possible; the front cross seat makes an ideal position in which to tie it. Lead two stays or guy ropes from the top of the mast back towards the stern, and delegate two men to hold the ends there and take the strain. You should *never* tie down such improvised rigging, as a sudden gust of wind could tear it from its moorings and damage the hull of the raft.

The heel or foot of the mast *must* be padded to prevent it chafing or punching a hole through the floor. The best way to do this is to pad it to ankle thickness, and then insert it into a

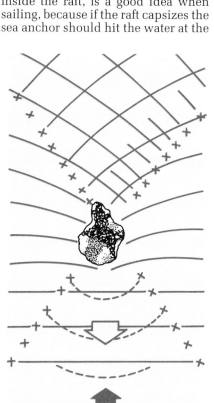

Island wave patterns

Waves are refracted as they approach land, and may give you your first indication that you are nearing it. By swimming or rafting with the waves and parallel to the slightly turbulent area marked 'X', you should reach land. If you have to swim on to a rocky shore, paddle with your hands while in a sitting position, with your legs in front of you so that if you do strike a rock you will hit your feet, not your head.

right angle to hold immediately from this position.

The risk of capsize should always be borne in mind in a life raft, and particularly when sailing. 'Running' before the wind with a very strong following sea is hazardous even in regular sailing because of the risk of being swamped or rolled head over heels, so don't try it in a raft. Distribute the weight of the passengers so that their weight holds the 'weather', or windward, side down; don't sit on the sides or stand up, and don't make sudden moves without warning. Lash all the movable gear down, and always keep the caps on water bottles or containers.

Capsize manoeuvres

If you do capsize, try to manoeuvre into the lee of the craft, and in multi-place rafts grab the righting handles so that you are hauling the opposite, weather, side upwards; the wind will then assist you. Once the vessel is right side up again, one man should work his way round to the weather side and hold it down while the others climb in over the lee, grasping the seats for leverage or using a boarding ladder if available.

Without help, the best place to board a raft is over the end. If the wind is blowing, board the raft with the wind at your back, and if you are boarding a one-man raft climb in from the narrow end, sliding up as nearly horizontal as possible.

Both bottom and top of a 20-man raft are identical, so you will not need to 'right' it, but you will need, of course, to recover equipment lashed to what is now the underside. The inflated boarding station fitted to these big craft will help.

Get back aboard as quickly and with as little panic as possible. Apart from other factors, thrashing about in the water, particularly if you are cut and bleeding, is one of the best ways to attract sharks. (They are also attracted by unusual noises such as underwater explosions, which is another good reason for rapidly getting into a raft from a sinking ship in a battle zone.)

Worldwide danger

You are likely to encounter sharks in practically any of the world's sea areas, including the Arctic and Antarctic, and even the most harmless will show interest in large floating objects such as a life raft. Of the 325 or so different varieties, only about 20 are known to attack man, and almost all of these are found in the tropic and sub-tropic seas between 4030 north and 4030 south latitude.

Only four – the great white, the mako, the tiger and the hammerhead – are likely to strike at a raft without provocation, though any shark more than about a metre long should be considered dangerous. All of them have voracious appetites and most hunt living animals, homing in on vibrations and scents such as blood. Some sharks hunt singly, but the most common reported attacks on man come when two or more are present, so a sharp look-out for several dorsal fins should be kept.

If you are in the water, group up

Above and above right: Rescue for a family shipwrecked off Mexico during 1987: they managed to attract the attention of the liner Canberra.

with other swimmers so that you can maintain an all-round watch and combine to ward off any attack.

Keep your clothes on, including footwear; evidence shows that sharks prefer semi-naked victims, and will snap at unprotected areas such as hands and feet. Clothing also protects you from painful abrasions caused by the shark's sandpaper-like skin. Splashing, slapping the water repeatedly with cupped hands, and roaring and yelling underwater will often turn a shark away.

If you have a knife, use it on the shark's vulnerable eyes and gills; a shark's back and sides are tough, and – contrary to popular myth – it does not have to turn sideways, exposing its softer underbelly, to snap at prey. Don't try to stab it head-on, in the nose: your blow is more than likely to be deflected onto its ragged teeth.

Keep your hands in

If you are in a raft and you sight sharks, keep as still as possible and do not trail hands or equipment over the side. If you are towing fishing bait on a line – even if you have caught a fish – let it go. Sharks feed mainly during the day, so conduct any burials at night, and paddle away from the area.

If a shark makes a direct attack on the raft, shoot to kill if possible, or fire into the water nearby. If you have no firearms, hit the shark with anything hard available – use spearing motions if you use an oar and the impromptu weapon will be less likely to break.

Finally, forget Tarzan films: hitting the shark with your fist will damage you far more than it will the attacker, while presenting the beast with a tasty morsel!

Huddle for warmth

A group of people huddled together will reduce the rate of heat loss still further. Keep your heads out of the water and use your arms to link up over your lifejackets. Hug as close as possible to maximise body contact, particularly at the chest. Interweave your legs as well.

HELP (heat escape lessening posture)

If you find yourself in very cold water with no immediate chance of rescue, you must try to postpone the onset of hypothermia. The HELP position can reduce heat loss by up to 50 per cent. Keep your head and neck out of the water and cover your other high heat loss areas (trunk and groin) as best you can. Even a partial covering is better than none.

Mines and Grenades

A hapless dummy is fragged by a C3 'Elsie' anti-personnel mine. Although the dummy has disintegrated in the explosion, a human target will lose bits of the legs. Because blast strikes the line of least resistance you lose your foot where your boot stops, so ankle boots tend to mean loss of the foot but high combat boots will disappear with the rest of your shin.

Week Four of the Section Commanders Battle Course starts with a spectacular introduction to mines and grenades — but there's still plenty of physical testing to come. On Monday morning, the Royal Engineers give everyone a demonstration of the effects of several types of mine, including the C3 "Elsie" anti-personnel mine, an improvised Claymore, the Rapid Cratering Kit (RCK), Mk VII and bar mines, and even a simulated napalm bomb.

Although each has its own special use, the RCK and napalm are by far the most visually impressive of the bunch. The effect of some mines, although lethal for those in the immediate vicinity, is not always obvious when viewed from afar. But you *can* see the devastation caused by the RCK and the resulting displacement of earth. Equally impressive is the vivid orange fireball of exploding napalm. Both evoke murmurs of approval from the attentive audience.

Exercise Tank Kill

This is scheduled to begin later in the day. Preceded by a two-hour anti-armour ambush excercise, Tank Kill puts into practice the lessons you have learned.

At 0500 hrs the following morning, you get orders for a patrol to recce a section of road for a possible anti-armour ambush site.

Note the size of the Bergens and the additional kit carried when you set out on a tank ambush exercise. The target is recce'd between 0500 and 0800, then one of the cadre will be told to plan and lead the operation.

The recce takes only a couple of hours or so, with everyone back in the harbour area by 0800. At 1000, the candidate appointed as section commander briefs you in full on the forth-

Another dummy having a bad morning at the firepower demonstration: it vanishes completely in a simulated napalm explosion. Improvised mines filled with gravel, nails or petrol are called fougasses and are an old military as well as guerrilla weapon.

The firepower demonstration leaves little to the imagination. It is a sobering reminder of the power of modern weapons to destroy the human body.

coming operation – a straightforward ambush on a forest road known to be used by enemy armour. The move out to the objective is typical of other similar patrols in previous weeks. Avoiding roads and tracks wherever possible, you make the best use of the natural cover of the forest.

Arriving at the ambush area, everyone leaves their bergens at the FRV indicated by the section commander, who next leads an initial recce to site wire obstacles and place any ordnance out to the front. You are then allocated individual fire positions.

In position

This ambush has been set up on gently sloping ground overlooking a dirt road. A two-man 84-mm (Carl Gustav) AT team, concealed just inside the forest, will have a clear view of the lead vehicle when it hits an anti-tank mine buried in the far side of the road directly opposite their position. To their right are two 66-mm (LAW) men. To the left is the com-

mand group, consisting of the section commander and two riflemen – one of whom will be responsible for providing smoke during the attack.

On a hillock off to the left, and just below the RV, is the cover group. A long stop (bar mine) has been placed at the roadside to their left. Along with Elsie mines and punji sticks, a barbed-wire low entanglement has been pre-

pared to the front-right of the 66-mm position. Hidden in the undergrowth on your side of the forest, it is placed to hinder any counter-attacking troops who manage to de-bus from the second vehicle.

In position ready for the ambush: this is the 'smoke man' ready with a selection of pyrotechnics to cover your withdrawal after the attack on the enemy vehicles.

Fighting Fit

It is a credit to your instructors — and yourselves — that the ambush position is well-sited and well-prepared. Now – will it work?

You settle down to wait. After a short while there is the sound of an approaching vehicle. It must be a T-62 tank at least! You fidget behind your weapons . . . any second now . . . What the . . .?

A big truck, hauling a trailer piled high with logs, roars through the killing area in a cloud of dust. False alarm! Lucky for the driver it was an anti-*tank* mine he ran over!

Time passes. At last you detect another, more familiar sound. The enemy use armoured vehicles with engines that sound remarkably similar to your own Land Rovers, so you wait until you are certain that there will be no mistake.

The real thing

A weird-looking, turret-mounted *thing* drives into view. No doubt about it this time.

A thunderflash (the AT mine) goes off – your signal to open fire. Immediately, the 84-mm fires a single round into the lead vehicle's turret. The firer hurriedly reloads just in case another is heeded. Smoke grenades are thrown to cover your withdrawal. At the same time, first one, then the other 66-mm LAWs are fired at the second vehicle. Meanwhile, the cover group deals with several enemy who have leapt clear of the halted convoy. The rest of you rapidly loose off no more than a magazine each before breaking contact.

Now you use the smoke cover, sprinting through the forest towards the FRV, leaving the survivors of the ambush to blast away at your empty positions. A quick head-check assures the section commander that everyone's present. You then begin an unopposed withdrawal – a five miles' tab with full kit!

Testing time

The next day sees you back at Dering Lines, where you spend the morning learning about the theory of FIBUA and DIBUA. In the afternoon, you have to run a log race and complete part of an assault course. This counts in the inter-section competitions, which began in Week One with Exercises Cheshire Cat and Point to Point, and continued with Exercise Rock Fan.

A three-mile run first thing in the morning will round off the physical tests. You have to sit a mid and final written test. Points are awarded for each phase of the competition, and those in the section with the highest combined score are each awarded with a specially embossed sweat shirt.

Despite all the physical conditioning, the three-mile 'canal race' in the early hours of Thursday morning proves almost too much for a few candidates. Several who drop behind are loudly urged on by their mates. Others are pushed or pulled along in an effort to keep everyone together.

Most of you, however, succeed in keeping with your section through the initial uphill leg behind Dering Lines,

Top: The 'Fantasian' APC, target of your vehicle ambush. Middle: The five-mile high-speed tab away from the ambush position. Bottom: The assault course is one of the last formal physical tests you have to pass.

then towards Brecon before turning left, down towards the canal, which you follow back to camp.

Afterwards, you go for the final lesson of the day – a 90-minute lecture on first aid. This finishes at 1945. The rest of the day is your own!

Combat Report

Borneo
Bumped on a Recce Mission

Terry Wilkinson served with the British Army in Borneo during the confrontation with Indonesia in the 1960s. Here he describes a four-man recce patrol.

We had been in the jungle for five weeks. During that time we had neither washed nor shaved, and our uniforms were tattered, dirty and torn.

Our four-man patrol was being used for gathering intelligence. It was thought that a guerrilla camp was located within marching distance of our present position and our task was to locate that camp and note the enemy strength, both in manpower and weapons. This information was to be sent back to company HQ, then we would withdraw, allowing a larger force to take out the position.

Barry was acting as the lead scout, armed with the military version of a Remington pump-action shotgun. The rest of the patrol, including me, carried SMGs with spare magazines, allowing for a rapid change if the going got tough.

The jungle at night can be unbelievably dark. You can't even see your hand in front of your face. It is also impossible to move without making a great deal of noise, so all movement is restricted to daylight hours.

A burst of automatic fire

Dawn was beginning to break as we packed away our equipment and methodically scoured the ground for any signs of our presence. We walked for about three hours, with Barry again as lead scout. Every now and then we would stop and listen for enemy patrols.

Suddenly the silence was shattered by the sound of Barry's shotgun as he blasted off two rounds in quick succession. This was immediately followed by Barry screaming, "Peel off!" as he ran past us. The next man fired a quick burst with his SMG and ran back towards Barry, and Tash and I followed suit.

After running through the bush for about 10 minutes, we re-grouped and assessed the

When our patrol was bumped we were about seven miles from the nearest friendly forces. Unlike Vietnam, the jungle in Borneo had few natural landing sites and most had to be hacked out.

situation. Barry had come across a large enemy patrol. Fortunately, they had been more surprised than he had. We decided to bypass them and continue our mission. Our movements were now extra cautious: marching for five minutes, then stopping and listening for ten.

Without warning, there was a burst of automatic fire and Barry fell to the ground. We were enveloped in the noise and confusion of battle and the strong smell of cordite as automatic weapons opened up on us. Tash braved the heavy fire, grabbed Barry and started to drag him towards us as I shouted, "Bug out!"

Tash, half-carrying Barry, and Steve ran from the ambush area. I hurriedly laid grenades, with trip wires about two feet above the ground, and then quickly joined them. Barry's leg wound, fortunately, was only superficial, and he dressed it while I reported the situation to HQ over the radio. As I spoke, there were three loud explosions, followed by the screams of men in agony. Some of the enemy had found the grenades.

He was killed instantly

We were ordered to bug out and rendezvous with friendly forces about seven miles away. Seven miles is a long way in the jungle, so we had to prepare for a tough march. After lying up for the night, we began to march as soon as it was light. Although Barry was in pain, he had no problem keeping up with us. We were now making good progress and I estimated that we would be with friendly forces within three hours.

Tash was leading as we clambered over a large tree trunk. I heard one burst of automatic fire, then saw several bullets hit him in the chest and neck. He was killed instantly.

Many other weapons joined in as we attempted to return fire, but the odds were against us. There was no alternative but to bug out again. We were now about 30 yards from the enemy, but they were still on our trail. Bullets flew around us as the guerrillas fired in our direction and the shouts of command from their leader could be heard clearly above the noise. The only way we were going to escape was to split up. After throwing grenades in the guerrillas' direction, we scattered. I had to dump

Our patrol covered a very large area and we had no immediate support. When we ran into the enemy we had to rely on breaking contact and evading.

my Bergen to reduce weight.

It took me 28 hours to reach friendly forces. On my arrival at HQ there was no sign of Barry or Steve, and I assumed the worst. Two days later, I learnt that Barry had been shot again, this time in the side, but he had evaded the enemy by going to ground. After the guerrillas had passed him by, he was able to call in a chopper by using search and rescue beacons and was winched on board. Steve, sadly, had not been so lucky.

Barry and I were to undertake five more operations together in that jungle.

'Walk-Through, Talk-Through'

In week 4 of the course you revise your FIBUA drills with the aid of a lecture and a 'walk-through, talk-through' demonstration. Now it's time to put it all into practice with one of you leading the attack on an enemy-held house. Here the mousehole charge has blown a hole in the wall and the first assault group posts a (simulated) grenade into the ground floor.

After a morning spent attending another battle lesson, Week Four of the Battle Course ends with an exciting and fast-moving practical in house clearing. First, however, each section is led to a clearing for a re-cap on the subject.

Practising the drills

"You've had lectures on FIBUA," the SI begins. "You've seen films on how it's done. Now you're going to practise the drills. In fact, what you are going to do this afternoon cannot technically be called FIBUA as such. Because, as you can see, we have only three two-storey buildings. What we run through here is really house-clearing. You have to remember that in a typical built-up area you'll have to clear multi-storey flats and buildings, great big office blocks – one floor at a time, one street at a time . . ."

The SI continues with the lecture, reminding you how to approach a building and where to blow an entry hole before moving inside and clearing each room. He tests you with questions on the composition of a typical house-clearing team. Ideally, this might consist of a four-man cover group, equipped with two LSWs and two rifles, a couple of 66-mm LAWs and several grenades. The group covers the approach of the assault groups, and likely enemy escape routes.

The command group normally consists of the section commander and a link man. The latter passes on orders as required. The group should be equipped with a radio and smoke grenades as well as their personal weapons.

The two assault groups usually comprise two riflemen apiece. Along with grenades, the first team carries a mousehole charge for breaching one

Your target is a row of three simply constructed concrete buildings on the Sennybridge training area. The exercise is house clearance rather than FIBUA proper, since you do not have to worry about large numbers of other buildings surrounding your target.

WALK-THROUGH, TALK-THROUGH

Left: Racing forward towards the enemy-held building, the assault group gets up to the windowless side of the building where the defenders cannot shoot at them. A mousehole charge is placed against the wall.

Below: A grenade sails through the ground floor window. Remember to 'post' your grenade into the building rather than lob it from any distance. That way you avoid hitting the windowsill and having a live grenade bouncing back towards you.

windowless side of the building. You work fast, placing the mousehole charge in position at the front of the house before joining your mate behind cover around the corner.

Bang! The mousehole charge goes off. Immediately, you throw a couple of grenades in through the breach. Moments later they explode, and you leap into the smoke-filled building, fingers on the trigger, weapons set to auto. With backs against the wall you systematically shoot into corners and cubby holes and up through the ceiling.

Clearing the rooms

As the smoke begins to clear you realise that you are in the hallway. No enemy in sight. Right – let your mates on the outside know:

"Hall clear!"

Now, the commander and his link man enter the building. Close behind is the second assault group. They all join you in rapidly clearing the rest of the lower level, raking each room with automatic fire, and using grenades when necessary.

The place reverbrates with the sounds of shooting and detonating grenades. Dense, acrid smoke fills the house interior.

wall of the building. The second pair should carry a bangalore torpedo – a metal tube filled with explosive, and used to destroy wire defences and obstacles.

Having made sure that everyone knows what his job is, the SI then takes you on a walk-through, talk-through rehearsal, with each group practising its particular role as a house is "cleared". In reality, it's best to clear a building from the top down. For exercise purposes, however, it is really only practical for the section to work its way up from the ground floor.

Opening moves

You begin the exercise proper with each section in position ready for the initial assault. The attack opens with the cover group of the leading section laying down suppressive fire and smoke. Your first assault group quickly moves in against the blind,

As soon as the grenade explodes you charge inside, raking the room and ceiling with SA80s on full auto. It is very smoky and the din is incredible, but as section commander you must co-ordinate the attack and keep the momentum of the assault going.

Above: Upstairs an enemy machine gunner continues to put down rounds.

Victory! Having fed leaden death to all the defenders, you make sure you are covering all approaches. In this situation it is easy to relax and then get bounced out of your position by an enemy counterattack.

"Room clear!"

Okay, that's it. Ground floor clear, and no enemy located.

"Downstairs clear!"

You can hear a slow-firing medium machine-gun above you. The enemy are obviously alive and causing problems for the lads from your other two sections waiting to assault their own objectives.

Trouble upstairs

You now move towards the stairs, only to find your way blocked with barbed wire. The second assault group hurriedly deals with it, using the bangalore torpedo. Everyone moves back as far as possible while it blows away the obstruction. You then rush upstairs, firing as you go. A shadowy figure appears on the landing and fires a brief burst. You return fire and the enemy soldier promptly disappears.

"Stairs clear!"

From one of the rooms the machine-gun continues to harass those outside. Okay, there it is. Grenade! Bang! Right, inside, squeeze the trigger. The enclosed space of the tiny room amplifies the noise of your weapon as you empty half a magazine. Spent cartridge cases spill to the floor.

The enemy gun, a .30-cal Browning, is propped on a window ledge, its still-smoking barrel now pointing harmlessly skyward. Next to it is a slumped figure.

"Room clear!"

The last remaining room is now dealt with. Another defender collapses onto the debris of battle littering the floor.

"Room clear! House clear!"

Aftermath

Everyone is sweating and breathing heavily. A whistle blows – the signal to reorganise. Automatically, you take up positions at windows overlooking the surrounding area, and gratefully gulp deep breaths of fresh air. Outside, your cover group closes in, moving into fire positions around the captured building while it is carefully searched.

A good operation, well carried out. The other sections clear their own houses with similar efficiency.

At last, you are ordered into the open, where the SI briefs you, as usual, on the main points of the exercise. There are always a few details that need sorting out, but on the whole your instructor is pleased with your efforts. His praise makes everything seem worthwhile, and does wonders for the confidence of the appointed section commander who led the operation.

Next, it's back to camp for the start of a well-earned, long-weekend leave!

Getting your breath back while deployed outside the building, covering the blind spot. This time the instructors are pleased with your efforts, which is a satisfying end to Week 4 of the course.

Above: The enemy's Browning .30 cal machine-gun is brought back into action but under new management. Reorganisation must be quick, with ammunition sorted out and everyone deployed to defend the building.